Folktales of Bhutan

Folktales of Bhutan

Kunzang Choden

White Lotus
Bangkok   Cheney

White Lotus Co., Ltd
G.P.O. Box 1141
Bangkok 10501

Published 1994. First Edition

Printed in Thailand

Illustrations by Kunzang Dorji

Typeset by COMSET Limited, Partnership

ISBN 974-8495-96-5   White Lotus Co., Ltd.; Bangkok
ISBN 1-879155-24-9   White Lotus Co., Ltd.; Cheney

Foreword
by
Her Royal Highness Princess Sonam Chhoden Wangchuck

The world at large is quite familiar with the wealth of religious and other literature that exists in Bhutan. What is, however, not equally known or accessible is the rich oral tradition as a source of knowledge. Among ordinary Bhutanese, for whom the transition from oracy to literacy is not yet complete, the oral tradition is a powerful living medium of communication between one generation and the next. It ensures the survival of undocumented knowledge. By relying on the oral tradition, or "Khaju" in Dzonghkha, the "illiterate" Bhutanese have been able to benefit from folktales. In the villages of Bhutan, folktales are still told and people, mostly children, learn from this living tradition.

The art of listening to folktales and retelling them has, in my opinion been an important tool for the development of native eloquence and articulateness which we find in abundance among ordinary Bhutanese. It also enables people to find moral, philosophical, religious, mythical and romantic meaning in the stories.

Since the progress of modernization began some three decades ago there has been rapid change in many aspects of Bhutanese society. Inevitably the crucial role that the oral tradition has played in transmitting knowledge is also likely to decline. There is an apparent danger that the folktales and fables whose deep significance and origins we do not yet fully understand could disappear. It is already apparent that children are reared on folktales from distant places at the expense of local ones, which could begin a process of alienation from the local culture.

Therefore Kunzang Choden's book is a laudable step towards preservation of a rich and vibrant heritage contained in the little known and hitherto undocumented folktales of Bhutan. Her book should stimulate interest in the young and revive the memories of older generations so that the work of a comprehensive compilation of Bhutanese oral tradition becomes conceivable. It is my great pleasure to compliment the author who is the first Bhutanese person to have written such a book. I strongly recommend this pioneering book to all readers.

S. C. WANGCHUCK

To my children
Dolma, Dechen and Dhondup

Contents

Preface

In the Bhutanese tradition, stories, fables, and legends are not told but are unraveled (*shigai* in Bumthangkha) and released (*tangshi* in Dzongkha). To me these concepts of releasing and unraveling are invested with much significance. It means that storytelling is a continuous process (unraveling) and to be released stories must be alive and vibrant. Stories are, therefore, alive and continuous, not only in the minds of those who unravel and those who release them, but also in the minds of those who listen to them being unraveled and released. This oral tradition, transmitted by one generation to another, is thus the continuing and living thread that links one generation to another.

The nine years of childhood spent in Tang Ugen Choling was very short, especially in terms of how much time I could spend with my parents. The duties of feudal lords were by no means simple and a certain amount of dedication and sacrifice was necessary to live through the many intricacies and sensibilities of dealing with human beings, the most important of which was trying to keep everybody contented and the village in harmony. This took up much of my parents' time. I may have been better off than many of my friends from the village in many ways. But I was certainly deprived of much valuable time with my parents. This was made worse by their untimely deaths. I could be with my parents only at specified times of the day. I had to fill in the rest of the time on my own. So I did what the other children of the village did, and played games rich in fantasy and filled with imagination. Above all I shared one common bond with every child in the village and that was the intense love of stories, legends and fables.

As I reminisce now of the storytelling sessions, I see a circle of adults and children relaxing in the late afternoon sun, in the West Gate field of Ugen Choling *naktsang*, listening in rapt attention to every word of the storyteller. At other times it was in the evenings, sitting around a charcoal brazier in the flickering light of the *lawang*. As the flickering light cast remarkable arrays of shadows, the images from the stories came to life and became real. Our imaginations and fantasies knew no bounds. We could listen to the same stories again and again, enthralled, as if we were listening to them for the first time. The stories touched our lives so deeply that a good storyteller could evoke every kind of emotion from the listeners. There was tears in silence for the tragedies, peels of laughter at the comical episodes, anger at the injustice, and feelings of triumph at the victories of the heroes. There were also times when the younger children would lie down and rest their heads on the knees of the adults and drift off into easy sleep. Overall, these sessions were accessible, enjoyable, and meaningful. Only at that time I did not realize their importance in my life.

The stories enriched the world we lived in. Although we did not physically travel beyond the mountains that enclosed the Tang valley, in our minds, our worlds extended far beyond: like the characters in the stories we climbed many mountains and crossed many valleys where everything became possible. Spirits, ghosts, and *sinpos* lived and competed in wit and strength with the human beings. Animals spoke and interacted with the human beings, sometimes as their enemies but other times as helpful friends. There was life in the other worlds, which human beings could momentarily enter and obtain a glimpse of the world of gods, spirits, and subterranean beings. Magic and myth abounded and became almost inseparable from our realities. There were stories that extolled the universal virtues of compassion, humility, kindness, and integrity. Yet there were other stories that spoke of senseless cruelty and crude and deceitful acts. But it was the fairly consistent themes (especially in the *namthars* or religious stories, not included here) of the stories that impressed us the most. Good triumphed over evil, quiet humility won over loud braggadocio and the rich generally conceded to the poor.

Some of the stories stayed alive in my mind even during the fourteen years of my cultural exile in India (at boarding school), often providing me with a safe refuge and solace in times of loneliness and depression, in trying to adjust and later on to understand other cultures. Memories of the stories helped to keep the link to my roots and, therefore, gave me my identity. I knew who I really was even when I was trying to conform to being somebody else! Years later I made efforts to trace the storytellers of the village to familiarize myself again with some of the stories of which I was no longer so sure. During this time I came to the realization that the art of the oral tradition is definitely on the decline; worse still, the story sessions are rapidly being replaced by video sessions which screen popular films from Hollywood, Bombay, and Hong Kong. The flickering *lawang* is now being replaced by the flashing blue-white light of the television set. I was immensely saddened when an old man who had told me many stories in childhood said, "I have forgotten all those stories. But everybody these days watches videos. Why do you want me to tell old stories?"

As I realize the importance of the stories as a link to who I am and where I come from, I also realize how important they will be to my children. It is for them and others of their generation that I write these stories with the hope that they will be of some value in their lives to link up with their cultural base so that in knowing their base they may better understand and appreciate their own lives.

The storytelling sessions are not a one-way communication where the storyteller simply talks and the others passively listen. There has to be constant interaction. Beyond the sad expressions of *"ayi wha"* and the *"yaah lama"* of surprise, someone from among the listeners has to respond to every sequence of the story. After every sequence a listener must say, *"Aeii"* or *"tse ni"* in Bumthangkha, *"delay"* in Dzongkha. These literally translate to, "and then". Only when there is a response from the listeners will the storyteller continue the story with an exaggerated *"Tse n.i..i..i"* in Bumthangkha or *"dela..a..a..y"* in Dzongkha. This custom is to prevent the spirits from listening to the stories and stealing them. As long as a human being responds and indicates that the story is being listened to, the spirits cannot steal them.

Every Bhutanese story begins with *Dangbo* and *Dingbo*. These two terms are used either as nouns, as in *"Dangbo thik naki key whenda"* which would be equivalent to saying "there once was a *Dangbo* and a *Dingbo"*, or as indications of time, as in *"Dangbo Dingbo"* which would equate to "long long ago". The length of time is made more specific by sounding the words *Dangbo* and *Dingbo* long or short. So, *"Dangbo Dingbo"* said with a short sound indicates a shorter time than if said *"Dangbo..o..o Dingbo..o..o.."*, which would mean a long, long, long time ago. The close of a storytelling session is usually marked by a customary story about *Dangbo* and *Dingbo* themselves, and I have followed this practice in this book.

It is more than likely that many of the stories bear similarities to stories from around the world. In fact in some cases the likeness is striking as in the story of the "Lame Monkey" and the world-famous fairy tale "Puss in Boots". Considering the similarities that exist between two such vastly different countries/cultures as Bhutan and Germany, it is not surprising to hear similar stories told around the region, especially in Tibet, India, and Nepal. In fact it is difficult to tell where each story may have actually originated, because so many local characteristics have been attributed to the stories in every place where they are told that they become drastically or subtly different but definitely unique to the particular region. But my intention here is not to trace the origin of each story or seek out similarities and differences. I wish to simply release and unravel the stories I heard in my childhood and now remember.

The reader will notice how freely Dzongkha, Bumthangkha, Kurtoipkha and Tibetan phrases are interspersed in the stories. This is the actual case and, therefore, I have not restrained myself to using one language. I use the phrases as they appear in the original stories. The glossary provides explanations of such terms and phrases (indicated by bold italic in the text). As far as possible, I have given a brief translation of these words when they occur in the stories for the convenience of the reader.

Finally I wish to make only one request to the readers—do pause long enough to say *"tse ni"* or *"delay"* every now and then so that these stories may not be stolen and they may remain ours to keep and pass on.

Introduction

Drukyul is the name by which the Bhutanese refer to their country. Located in the eastern Himalayan zone, it covers an area of approximately 46,000 square kilometers. This landlocked kingdom is bounded to the north and northwest by the Tibetan regions of China and to the south by the Indian states of West Bengal and Assam. The spectacular mountainous terrain of Bhutan is easily one of the most rugged in the world, rising in altitude from a few hundred meters in the south to the permanently snow capped peaks in the north. These extremes of topography result in a diversity of temperatures and rainfall. Consequently the variety in flora and fauna, ranging from the subtropical to the alpine, is sensational.

This country of 600,000 people can be broadly divided into three ecological zones. The northern zone, bordering Tibet, where the peaks rise above 7,000 meters, is the most sparsely populated part of the country. This alpine region is inhabited by pastoralists, the Brokpas, who graze their sheep, cattle and yak up to elevations of 5,000 meters in the summer and migrate to lower areas in the winter. The Drukpas, who are of Mongoloid origin, live in the western part of the central zone. They are followers of the Drukpakagyu school of Buddhism from which the name of the country, Drukyul or land of the Drukpas is derived. Drukyul is also taken to mean land of the dragons (Druk means dragon). The eastern part of the central zone is home to the Sharchokpas (easterners). The Lhostampas or people of Nepali origin, who came to the country towards the end of the nineteenth century, live in the southern foothills which rise from the Indian plains. Over 90 percent of the population are engaged in subsistence farming, combining crops, livestock and forestry.

It is thought that Bhutan may have been inhabited as early as 2,000 BC. But in the absence of any archeological studies it is generally accepted that the two Buddhist temples, Kyichu Lhakhang in the Paro Valley and Jampa Lhakhang in the Bumthang Valley represent the only testimony to the country's earliest history. These temples are said to have been constructed by the Tibetan King Srongtsan Gompo, who ruled Tibet from about 627 to 649. The most important religio-historical event in Bhutan's history was the arrival of Padmasambhava, a Tantrist from Swat (in present-day Pakistan) in the eighth century. Commonly known as Guru Rinpoche or Precious Teacher, he introduced Tantric Buddhism and is considered by the Nyingmapa religious school as the second Buddha. Prior to his arrival the people seem to have been animists. The subsequent period, up to the seventeenth century, was marked by the activities of many saints and scholars who left their influence upon the country in various ways.

Shabdrung Ngawang Namgyel (1595–1651) unified the country and introduced a sophisticated administrative and legal system. He established the dual system of government consisting of a state clergy headed by the Je Khenpo (chief abbot) and the desi (temporal leader). He initiated the building of dzongs or fortresses which not only housed monasteries but also were the seat of the regional governments. The majestic dzongs, which may still be seen all over the country, not only bear witness to the architectural skills of that time but also are treasure troves of exquisite sculpture, paintings, and frescoes. They still serve as the seat of the local administration under the district administrator or *Dzongdha*. The dual system was replaced by a hereditary monarchy in 1907. His Majesty King Jigme Singhe Wangchuck is the fourth hereditary king.

For political reasons and also because of its almost inaccessible and rugged terrain, Bhutan survived in self-imposed isolation until the late nineteen fifties. In the few decades since Bhutan has opted to emerge from its isolation, it has made considerable progress in its efforts to modernize. Changes have reached every aspect of Bhutanese society. While the Bhutanese are willing to forge ahead and keep up with the changing times, they also see themselves as upholders of Buddhist values as well as their own traditions and ancestral customs. They dearly cherish the goal of finding a balance between tradition and modernization and the influence of this aspiration is apparent not only in the life styles of the people but also in all the policies of the government.

Bhutan was opened to tourism in 1974. Although tourism brings in much needed currency, it is restricted. The lack of infrastructure and tourist facilities s well as Bhutan's efforts to preserve her natural and cultural heritage are the main reasons for the restrictions. Individual travelers cannot visit the country unless officially invited by the government. All tourists must come to Bhutan through one of the government approved travel agencies. The guide book *Bhutan the Himalayan Kingdom* by Françoise Pommaret published by Passport Books is highly recommended for accurate and detailed information on the country.

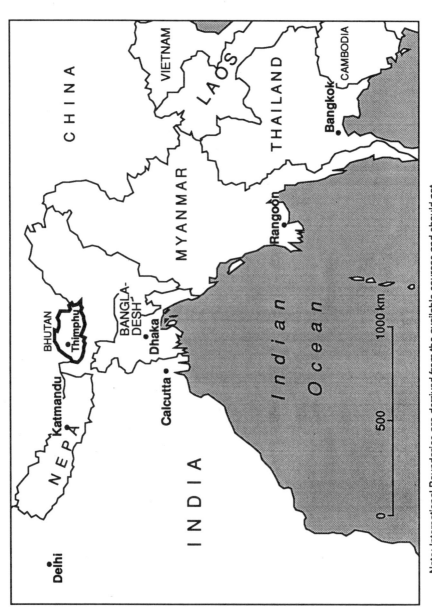

Note: International Boundaries are derrived from the available sources and should not be taken as authoritative. This is to show only the geographical location of Bhutan.

Part 1
Folktales

Mimi Heylay Heylay

Dangbo..o..o Dingbo..o..o.. Mimi Heylay Heylay was out in the hot sun digging in a field. Mimi Heylay Heylay or grandfather Heylay Helay, as he was affectionately known to all the villagers, was a man of no outstanding physical stature but an impressive personality. His frail body was balanced delicately on his bowed legs with calves that bulged boldly. He could be seen at all the village gatherings stroking his goatee made up of a few strands of hair. This jolly old man was not given to hard work and he had lived for many years on the good will of his fellow villagers. The slow half-hearted movement of his hoe was a clear indication that he did not enjoy the tedious and backbreaking job of preparing the buckwheat field. Therefore he was visibly annoyed when he was suddenly faced with a huge tree stump which stood menacingly in the middle of the field. He stood there looking at it pensively, all the while stroking his goatee. He decided that it had to go. So he began to attack it. Little by little he dug out the roots and then began to pull and tug at it until sweat poured down his brow and his palms were blistered and aching. Just as the sun was descending behind the western mountain ranges he gave it one final tug and the whole stump came out with a terrific crash.

In the now gaping hole where the tree root had once been, he at once saw a large flat circular turquoise which looked like a *golang* or a flat pan for making the famous *Bumthangpa khuli*. He could hardly believe his eyes. With his eyes wide open he stood there staring at it in awe for a long time. Finally he up picked this heavy turquoise piece and scrutinized it. It was truly the most beautiful thing he had ever seen!

The owner of the rooster was rather astonished but this was an offer he could not refuse.

Mimi Heylay Heylay said aloud to himself, "Now that I have this turquoise, I don't have to work any more. I'll sell it to get rich." With his newly acquired wealth and confidence, Mimi Heylay Heylay swaggered to the market. On the way to the market he met a man who was leading a horse on a rope.

The man asked, "Where are you going, Mimi Heylay Heylay?"

Mimi Heylay Heylay sang, "Don't say Mimi Heylay Heylay; instead listen to what I have to tell you. I dug a field where I came across a tree stump, I pulled out the stump and I found a turquoise, so now I am going to sell it in the market. Would you like to exchange your horse for my turquoise?"

The man was completely taken aback. Had this old man gone mad? The turquoise was priceless. This was an opportunity not to be missed, so he quickly agreed and the exchange was made. The man with the turquoise walked away rapidly, afraid that Mimi Heylay Heylay would change his mind. But Mimi Heylay Heylay, who was perfectly happy with the deal, continued his journey, leading the horse by the rope. He had not walked very far when he met a man with a bull who asked, "Where are you going, Mimi Heylay Heylay?"

Mimi Heylay Heylay once again sang, "Don't say Mimi Heylay Heylay; instead listen to what I have to tell you. I dug a field where I came across a tree stump. I pulled out the stump and I found a turquoise, which I exchanged for this horse, now would you like to exchange your bull for the horse?"

The man gaped in total disbelief, for his old bull was a poor bargain compared with the handsome young stallion. But he quickly got over the initial shock and hastily made the exchange. After the exchange was made, Mimi Heylay Heylay led the bull by the rope which was tied around its horns and continued on his way to the market. Soon he met a man with a ram who asked him where he was going. This time Mimi Heylay Heylay sang, "Don't say Mimi Heylay Heylay; instead listen to what I have to tell you. I dug a field where I came across a tree stump. When I pulled out the stump I found a turquoise. I have exchanged the turquoise for a horse. I exchanged the horse for a bull. Now would you like to exchange your ram for my bull? The owner of the ram was surprised but happily agreed and quickly led the bull away. Mimi Heylay Heylay walked on with the gait of a successful trader, pleased that he had been able to make such quick and smooth barters within a short time. The ram followed his new master reluctantly, bleating loudly.

By and by he met a man with a rooster under his arm. When the owner of the rooster asked him where he was going Mimi Heylay Heylay as usual sang, "Don't say Mimi Heylay Heylay; instead listen to what I have to tell you. I was digging a field where I came across a tree stump. When I removed the stump I found a turquoise. I exchanged the turquoise for a horse which was exchanged for a bull and the bull for a ram, now would you like to exchange your rooster for my ram?"

The owner of the rooster was rather astonished but this was an offer he could not refuse. He gladly took the ram and gave his bird to Mimi Heylay Heylay. Mimi Heylay Heylay tucked the rooster under his arm with a flourish and walked on until he met a man who was singing to his heart's content as he walked along. When he saw Mimi Heylay Heylay he stopped singing to ask him where he was going and once again Mimi Heylay Heylay sang, "Don't say Mimi Heylay Heylay; instead listen to what I have to tell you. I was digging a field where I came across a tree stump. When I removed the stump I found a turquoise. I exchanged it for a horse, the horse for a bull, the bull for a ram, the ram for a rooster. Now would you like to exchange your song for the rooster? Thoroughly surprised the singer stood there quite dumbfounded. Mimi Heylay Heylay[1] happily thrust the bird into the arms of the lucky singer and walked away singing to his heart's content, "*Shom a lay laymo, ow lay pey owlay pey......ow lay pey....*"

---

[1] A person is often compared to Mimi Heylay Heylay when he/she makes obviously silly deals.

Tsongpon Dawa Zangpo

Dangbo..o..o Dingbo..o..o.. there was a widow who lived with her three sons. Their father had been a prosperous merchant. But after his death the family had fallen on hard times. So when the sons grew up the mother wanted them to become traders, hoping that they could have at least some of their former prosperity.

One day she called them together and said, "Your father was a very successful merchant and I am sure that you too can become like him. Go into the world and become merchants."

To help them start off their business she gave each of them something that she had saved over the years. Even in times of dire need she had held onto these things for her sons. She gave a gold coin to her oldest son, a silver coin to her middle son, and three rolls of woolen fabric to her youngest.

The three sons decided to go in different directions and start their trades. So they bade farewell to their mother and each other and went their different ways. The youngest son whose name was Dawa Zangpo had not gone very far when he chanced to come across some boys tormenting a cat. They pulled and poked at it and the cat staggered and meowed pathetically. At once he was very sorry for the cat. "*Aye di chi*, poor thing, please stop tormenting this poor animal," he said to the boys, but they would not pay any heed to his pleas. Finally he offered them a roll of the woolen fabric in exchange for the life of the cat. At this the boys agreed and let the cat go. He picked up the cat and stroked it gently and the cat feebly licked his hand in response.

In the same way he saved a dog with the second roll of fabric and a monkey with the third. Now he had nothing to trade with. So he

7

As he looked on, the waters of the lake swished about and a circle of ripples appeared in the center of the lake as a beautiful woman came out.

traveled around aimlessly with the three animals until one day he reached the shores of a great lake. There was a group of fishermen who were wildly excited because they had caught a big fish. The fish was still alive and wriggling in the sand. Full of loud enthusiasm they were about to cut it up and divide the meat among themselves. Dawa Zangpo was overcome with compassion for the fish, so he begged them to spare its life. The fishermen were quite amused. "What will you give us if we let this fish go?" they ridiculed.

All he had to offer were the clothes on his back and he at once readily took these off to give them. When they realized how serious he was they sheepishly took the fish and released it into the water and walked away with his clothes. The fish floated for a while then slowly steadied itself and swam away, quite unsure of itself.

As soon as the fishermen were gone there was a strange sound from the lake. As he looked on, the waters of the lake swirled and swished about and a circle of ripples appeared in the center of the lake as a beautiful woman came out. "I have been sent to call you by the *luyi gyalpo*, the king of the subterranean world. He would like to reward you for saving his daughter."

For a while this spartan man stood on the banks of the lake speechless with wonder. Finally he fed his animals and said, "All right, now I am ready to come."

He closed his eyes as he was bidden to do and held onto the sleeves of the woman as she plunged back into the water. "The king will offer you everything that you could wish for but you must ask only for the ring on the finger of his right hand," whispered the woman as they reached the turquoise gate of the *luyi gyalpo's* palace. Strains of a plaintive and melancholic music from a lone flute greeted his ears as he walked carefully on the turquoise floors that shone in the pale, shimmering light that filtered in through the water.

He soon found himself in the presence of the subterranean king. He had the upper body of a human being but his lower body was a massive snake that slithered and swayed gently. He was the *lu shiwa* or the peaceful *lu*. He smiled benignly under a halo of serpents. He had another serpent around his neck that crawled sluggishly. Dawa Zangpo was given milk and puffed buckwheat as a welcome offering.

After three days in the underworld Dawa Zangpo begin to worry about his friends on earth and so he asked the lu, " Please let me go back to my world. I have been away from my friends for too long and they must be hungry."

The *lu* at once offered him gold, silver, and all sorts of gems but he declined all offers, saying, "If you really wish to give me something I would like to have the ring from the finger of your right hand."

The lu gave him the ring very reluctantly as the ring was a wish-fulfilling ring, and yet this man had saved the life of his only daughter.

Back on earth Dawa Zangpo was very happy to see that all three animals were well. After having fed them he decided to try out the ring and wished for a house on the island in the middle of an immense lake. No sooner had he made the wish then he found himself on the island in a beautiful palace surrounded by servants who waited to serve his every need.

Now the king of the West who up to now had been the most powerful and most wealthy man in all the land at once felt threatened by somebody who seemed to possess supernatural powers. He was jealous and curious to find out how a *dzong* (palace) had been built overnight on the island. He asked for a volunteer to go across the lake and find out how everything had happened. Nobody would volunteer as the way was fraught with perils and it was said to be an endless journey of no return. Finally a *gomchen* who had mastered some tantric powers came forward. The king was of course very pleased and rewarded him generously.

The *gomchen* finally reached the island but it had taken him a long time. Once on the island he pretended to be a beggar and went to beg at the gate of Dawa Zangpo's *dzong*. The latter who was rather surprised but pleased to see a visitor asked him to stay on. The *gomchen* stayed on and soon found out the secret of the ring. Every day for three years, the *gomchen* trailed Dawa Zangpo, waiting for an opportunity to steal the ring but he never took it off his finger. The *gomchen* would have failed, had not a stroke of good fortune come to his aid. It happened while Dawa Zangpo was having his bath and the hot water swelled his fingers and he took off the ring till the swelling went down. It was at this moment that the *gomchen* snatched up the ring and wished to be taken across the lake to the palace of the king of the West. The wish-fulfilling ring at once granted his wish and before he could blink his eyes he was in the presence of the powerful king of the West. The king of the West was once again the most powerful person, but with the magical ring now in his possession his powers had multiplied many times. The *gomchen* was rewarded handsomely and made the prime minister to the king.

The instant the ring was taken the palace vanished and Dawa Zangpo had nothing except the three animals. The cat, being the most intelligent of the three, called the other animals together and pointed out, "Now is our chance to show our gratitude to this gentle compassionate man. We must think of a way to get back the ring." The three animals sat together and after a long discussion they agreed upon a plan. The dog being a good swimmer agreed to carry the other two and swim across the lake. Once they reached the western kingdom each animal immediately proceeded to carry out his assignment. So the dog crouched behind a bush and kept watch. The monkey went into the king's maize field and began to destroy the entire crop, pulling down the stalks and breaking off the cobs. The gardener, seeing the ravage, immediately reported the incident to the king, who was a keen hunter. He summoned all his men together and went after the monkey. While the palace was thus unattended the cat crept into the palace, lay down near the securely locked door of the *gyalpoi bangzoi* or royal treasure trove and pretended to be dead. The mice in the palace were greatly excited and mystified over the death of a cat they had never seen before and they reported the matter to their king and sought counsel from him. The mouse king immediately came to look at the strange dead cat. He peered at it. The cat stayed very still. All the mice watched and held their breaths as their brave king went closer to the cat. Seeing that all his subjects were watching him he ventured even closer and actually began to poke and pull at it. The cat suddenly sprang up, caught the king and declared, "Your king is my prisoner, I will not release him until you bring me the new ring that the king of the West has recently acquired."

The mice scurried about in the palace looking everywhere for the ring. Soon the ring was found and brought to the cat who promptly released the mouse king. The cat then went off with the ring to join his two friends in the forest. The monkey held the ring in his hand and the three animals set out across the lake on their return journey. As they were about to reach the shore, a sudden wave splashed over them and the ring was swept out of the monkey's hand into the lake. Just then a fish came swimming by and swallowed the ring. No sooner had it swallowed it than a waterfowl swooped down and caught the fish. The dog had seen all this and knew exactly what to do, while his two friends bemoaned their ill luck. The dog ran after the startled bird who dropped the fish from its beak and flew into the sky. The dog quickly recovered the ring from the fish and instantly took it to Dawa Zangpo, who was so overcome with joy and gratitude that he fainted.

From then onwards the four friends lived in peace and prosperity for the rest of their lives and Dawa Zangpo decided never to take the ring off his finger at all.

The Cuckoo and the Frog

Dangbo..o..o Dingbo..o..o.. there was a big, fat ugly frog who was married to a cuckoo. The cuckoo could never fathom the frog's feelings for her. He was always strange and often quite suspicious. She longed to find out what he actually thought about her. So one day she cheerfully said, "I want to go and visit my relatives in Tibet." The frog nodded his big unsightly head impassively and belched out a barely comprehensible, "Go".

She said good-bye to the frog and presently flew off in the direction of the high mountain ranges to the north of Bhutan. She fluttered in the air for a while and when she was sure the frog could no longer see her she swooped down and flew back on to a tree near the pond. Carefully hidden among the thick foliage of the tree, the cuckoo kept a close watch on the frog. It was a warm sunny day and it was not long before the frog jumped up upon a large lily pad. He stretched out his limbs in all directions and gave a loud yawn and after he had made himself comfortable he basked at his leisure in the sun. While he lay there he scornfully mumbled to himself, but loud enough for the other creatures in the pond to hear:

> Cuckoo, Cuckoo, my Cuckoo,
> She must now be climbing over the *Monla karchung*
> Her front must be soaked in *chabsang*,
> And her back must be rotting with her sweat.

The pond soon resounded with the loud laughter and snide giggles of the other inhabitants of the pond. The frog seemed to

13

There was a big, fat and ugly frog who was married to a cuckoo.

enjoy this immensely and kept repeating the same derogatory re-marks over and over again. Seeing and hearing all this the cuckoo shook her head in shame and humiliation as her eyes welled up with tears. So, this is what he thought of her! Suddenly, she flew out from her hiding place and confronted him, quivering with emotion.

"It's not been a whole day since we parted and this is how you ridicule and disgrace me. From now on I shall have nothing to do with you." The frog was taken by surprise and lay there staring at her with his bulging eyes that bulged even further. How repulsive and disgusting he looked! How could she have endured him so long? He was so ashamed of himself that he leapt into the water with a big splash and never came out again.

"The water has been defiled with your lowly presence. I shall not drink it even if I have to die of thirst,"[1] continued the cuckoo.

And the peculiar marriage between the frog and the cuckoo was thus terminated.

---

[1] Many Bhutanese believe that the cuckoo does not drink water from ponds. Early in the mornings one can often see the cuckoo drinking the dewdrops on the grasses and the leaves.

For the third time he carried his wife's body until he reached the banks of a huge river.

The Hoopoe

Dangbo..o..o Dingbo..o..o… somewhere in the wilderness of the Bhutanese forests, signs of winter were everywhere. Many trees stood bleak and leafless and a chilling wind blew rentlessly. Like the other birds and beasts in the forest a hoopoe couple was busily preparing for the lean and cold months. They made their nest warmer and began to stock up grains and whatever else they could find so that they would not starve during the harsh winter months.

While the male hoopoe flew around and collected whatever he could, the task of arranging the stores in their nest fell on the female hoopoe. Now one day while she was piling up the grains, a precious pea which her husband had so proudly brought home just the day before fell from her beak into a deep crevice of the stone wall in which they had built their nest. She tried to get it out but the pea was too deep down for her even to see it. By the end of the day, although her beak was raw and scarred, the pea was still deep inside the crevice.

At dusk when birds come home to roost, the male hoopoe came with his collection for the day. He proudly surveyed their stock. "One pea is missing. You must have eaten it, you ungrateful *moringmo*," he accused her. He was tired, and easily worked himself into a fury. He ruffled up his feathers and scolded her, and as if that was not enough he began to peck at her and push her around until she was dead. Instantly the male hoopoe regretted what he had done.

He looked at the still body of his dear wife for a long time in utter disbelief. "I will take her body to a safe and clean place," he decided. At last he sighed to himself and then lifted the dead body onto his back and began the long and arduous journey. After flying for a long time he perched on the top of a tree on a high mountain. He thought, "This may be a good place for my wife." Just then he saw some vultures circling the skies so he sang,

> The mountains are the home of the gods,
> They are sacred and clean,
> Yet the vultures hover above,
> This will not be a good resting place for my wife.

He once again took up his precious burden and flew over great distances. His wings ached and his body grew heavy so he rested on a great boulder in a huge plain. He looked around and considered the place. Alas, a family of mice were scurrying about so he sang,

> The plain is vast,
> It's where the paths of thousands of travelers meet
> And dangers abound.
> The mice are waiting eagerly to devour my wife
> I will not leave her here.

For the third time he carried his wife's body until he reached the banks of a huge river. He perched on a large log of wood on the bank of the river and looked around. He saw the fish swishing about as they swam in the water and he sang,

> The river flows swiftly
> Carrying down everything with it.
> It would carry my wife down too
> But the fish would eat her before that.
> I will not leave her body here.

"No place is good enough for my wife," he sighed sadly as he lifted up the beloved remains of his wife and continued his journey again, flying over high mountains and swooping into deep valleys. But his search proved to be futile and he decided to return to his nest. He had spent the whole winter carrying his wife's dead body around so that when he reached home it was already early spring. Worn out from his long unsuccessful journey, he feebly laid his wife's body down on the rock in front of the entrance to their nest and looked in. He could not believe what he saw. The single pea that had fallen into the crevice had grown and was now flowering. It filled up their whole nest. This was far too much for someone who had already suffered so intensely. He was overcome with remorse and exhaustion, and fell down dead beside the body of his wife.

She was a young girl with long hair flowing in all directions.

The Boys who Went to Buy Cows

Dangbo..o..o Dingbo..o..o.. in the eastern highlands of Bhutan there was a village. It was a prosperous village, for each household had some plots of land on which they cultivated maize and millet and they also owned a few heads of cattle. In those days a person's wealth was counted by the number of cattle one possessed, so acquiring more cattle was a prime preoccupation of most of the villagers.

Now it happened that there was a very rich woman in this village who had a son. They already had a large number of cattle but they wanted more. There was also a poor woman with a son who had no cattle at all. One day the two boys met together and agreed to go and buy some cattle. The rich boy had a *dri*, a measure of gold dust, and the poor boy had only three worn-out copper coins.

When all the preparations were made the two boys set out further eastwards. They traveled for many days together, crossing many valleys, and climbing many mountains. Finally they decided that they should part and go their separate ways. The rich boy took the big and smooth path while the poor boy had to take the small and stony path. Before he took the path he planted his walking stick in the ground and prayed that if he should achieve his goal the stick should come to life.

The poor boy walked for many days, past innumerable ravines and gorges, across mountains that reached for the skies and deep, deep valleys that sunk into the earth's surface until one day he reached a solitary house in a narrow valley. The house stood beside a turbulent river that roared and gushed down the valley. He went into the house and there he saw an old man and an old woman. They were both blind. They were sitting together and sharing a meal. The old man would pass a handful of rice to the old woman, and the old woman would pour some *tsaoem*, a stew-like mixture of meat and vegetables into the old man's *phob* or cup. The poor boy, who had not had a proper meal since he left his home, quietly sat down between the old couple and ate all the food that was being passed. Soon the old couple sensed his presence there and without any warning the old man suddenly got up and shut the door. He then began to feel and grope around the house until they caught the boy. The boy begged them to forgive him. "I was so hungry and I made a mistake. Please have mercy on me and I will do whatever you tell me to do."

The old couple spared him and told him to look after their cattle. "Herd our cattle well and in due course we will reward you. Be warned, keep the cattle away from the *sinpos'* fields or you too will be blinded like us. "

The boy was a good herder and he looked after the cattle with the proficiency of an experienced cowherder for he had frequently herded the villagers' cows. The old couple grew fond of him and wished that he would stay with them. But the boy would not agree, for he desired nothing more than to return to his own village and be with his mother.

One day while he was with the cattle he had a strange idea, "What would happen if I let these cattle go into the *sinpos'* fields?" he mused. He was so excited by the idea that he actually began to drive his cattle towards the forbidden fields belonging to the *sinpos*. It was not long after the cattle began to munch away at the lush green mustard plants that there was a shrill whistle and a warning, "Get your cattle out of our fields. Ya, ya, don't let me come to you."

The boy pretended not to hear the warning and soon the *sinpos'* daughter came to him. She was a young girl with long hair flowing in all directions. There were fangs in her mouth and her breasts hung down to her waist. The boy was horrified by the sight but he mustered all his courage and kept his calm. Now as the fields were quite far away from the *sinpos'* house, the daughter was hot and tired after the long walk. So she sat in the shade of a tree panting and gasping and said, "I am going to rest for a while and then I will see what I can do with you. Right now come here and pick the nits from my hair," she commanded, so confident that she had the boy in her control. "Get all the nits out but don't you dare to touch the louse; it's my *sog*, my life force," she added. The *sinpo* girl had foolishly placed herself in her adversary's hands.

The boy pretended to pick out the nits but actually he looked for the louse. When he found it he caught it and tried to see if it was really the girl's *sog*. He held it between his thumb and forefinger and squeezed it and the girl rolled up her eyes and life seemed to drain out of her. He squeezed it harder and harder until the girl stopped breathing altogether. The boy knew that the *sinpos* would be coming to look for their daughter so he began to dig a pit. He made the pit very deep and then covered it with twigs and leaves so that they would not see it.

Sure enough when the *sinpos* realized that their daughter had not returned they came to look for her. The boy had concealed himself in the thick branches of a tree and waited and watched. The *sinpos* came sniffing and searching for their daughter. They looked even more terrifying than the daughter. The father had fangs so long that one scratched the ground and the other reached high above his head. The mother's hair was long and matted and flew wildly in all directions as she ran. Her breasts were so long that she carried them over her shoulders and they kept slipping off and touching the ground and she had to continuously lift them up and heave them over her shoulders. They were so intent on finding their daughter that they did not notice the covered pit and they fell into it with a tremendous crash. They begged to be released.

"First of all you, have to tell where I can find the eyes of *mimi* and *aila*," demanded the boy.

"The eyes are in the *phuta* which has been turned upside down on the shelf near the stove in the kitchen."

The boy went into the house to look for the eyes and indeed they were in the *phuta*. But of course he had no intention of letting the *sinpos* out of the pit so he went back to the pit and filled it up with soil and boulders until he was sure that they would never be able to get out again. Now he had to fit the eyes of the old couple. He took the eyes out of the *phuta* and blew away the dust from them and soaked them in water for they were quite dry by now. Then he began to fit the eyes into the eye sockets of the old man.

"Can you see yet, Mimi?" he asked, as he put them back into the hollows of the eye sockets.

"A little," replied the old man with uncertainty.

The boy carefully readjusted them until the old man exclaimed with delight, " I can see better than before!"

In the same way he fixed the old woman's eyes. The old couple was grateful to the boy and asked him what he wanted in return for his help. He said he wanted nothing but the golden horn. The boy knew about this horn because he had come across it in the attic and had heard about its magical powers. When the horn was sounded all cattle within hearing distance would follow the sounds. The old couple sadly handed the horn to the boy, but advised him, "Please blow the horn only in the deep valleys and never on the mountain tops." The old couple hoped that this way all the cattle would not hear the sound.

The boy said, "Ya, ya" and slinging the horn across his back, he started his journey homewards. When he reached the highest peak, he stood firmly with his legs apart, inhaled the thin crisp mountain air deeply, and then blew into the horn loud and clear. Hundreds of beautiful young *jatsams* heard the sound and followed it. All he had to do was round them up and drive them towards his home.

After several days he arrived at the place where he had parted with the rich boy. The peach stick he had planted had now grown into a small tree and it was full of pink blossoms. He took this to be an auspicious sign and was happy. Soon the rich boy arrived, but he had only some poor looking *bachu* with him. The rich boy was shocked and filled with instant jealousy when he saw the poor boy with his herd. He wondered how the poor boy had managed to get such a wonderful herd for his three copper coins while he could only get a handful of sickly *bachu* for the capital he had. He could not bear to face the humiliation and the shame of meeting his family and the other villagers. His wicked mind soon began to plot and plan on how to get rid of the poor boy.

They were still a few days from home and the rich boy was determined to eliminate his friend. One night while they camped he pretended to be full of concern for his friend and insisted that as it was a cold night he should sleep close to the fire so that he would be warmer. The poor boy did not suspect anything and slept close to the fire and gratefully watched the starry skies before he drifted into a deep sleep. The rich boy began to feed the fire until it was blazing fiercely and then he suddenly kicked his friend into the fire. The blazing fire quickly consumed the body of the poor boy and there was not a telltale sign of the foul deed.

In the morning there was nothing left of the poor boy except a handful of ashes. The rich boy seized the magic horn and blew it, and all the animals came together, but a beautiful young milking *jatsam* would not join the rest. She kept on searching around the camp site as if looking for a missing calf. When she saw the site of the fire she resolutely went there and began to lick up all the ash, every speck of it.

After she had licked up all the ash she began to sneeze. She sneezed, once, twice, and at the third time the poor boy was reborn through her nostrils. He was reborn as an exceptionally handsome man. He was just the right height and the right weight, rather square, every woman's dream man! He was wearing a wonderful blue woolen *gho* and his *lagi* was pure white. He was wearing *dhalham* and looked every bit like a dashing young *dasho*. The rich boy now began to panic and he was wretched. The poor boy did

25

not say anything to him but on the last day of their journey he took the rich boy by surprise and set him ablaze too.

The following day while the poor boy prepared to leave camp one of the bachu began to lick up the ashes and began to sneeze, once, twice, and at the third sneeze out came a little cretin who was not only very small but also exceedingly ugly. When the two boys reached their village the women came out with *marchang*, the ceremonial welcome drink. The mother of the rich boy, who was confidently standing close to the hundred wooden sticks she had driven into the ground to hobble their cattle, had a very nasty shock. As the rich boy drove the sickly *bachu* towards her she fainted in extreme bewilderment and humiliation. The poor boy's mother had cried so much with worry for her son that her eyes were now full of fungi. She had driven only one stick into the ground, for she had expected nothing more, but now she watched in amazement as the *jatsams* were driven towards her and she was absolutely ecstatic.

The Hen and the Monkey

Dangbo..o..o Dingbo..o.. it happened once that a monkey and a hen lived together. The monkey did all the work in the field and the hen kept the house and prepared the food. The monkey had to work hard in the fields and he was always tired. It aggravated him no end that every time he came home, the house was clean, there was food kept warm in the hearth and the hen was always sitting in the corner of the room and slumbering peacefully.

He thought, "I always have to do the hard work while hen has nothing to do and can sleep all day. Tomorrow I will ask her to change jobs." The next day the hen went to the fields. With the hoe balanced delicately on her back she walked away briskly. The monkey tried to clean the house but did not know how to. He tried to cook but he could not even start the fire. At the end of the day he was not only tired but also very angry for the house had not been swept and there was no food for the hen when she came home.

The next day the monkey said that he had changed his mind and wanted to go to the field again. Actually he wanted to see how the hen did her work. He hid in the trees and watched her. The hen spent the whole morning picking and scratching in the dirt looking for food for herself. Then she went into the house and deftly flapped her wings and swept the floors. Then she rekindled the fire from the embers in the hearth. Next she set a pan on the stove, put some butter in it and let it melt. When the butter had melted and was hot she climbed on to the beam above the hearth and laid an egg into the pan with a neat splash. She got down and picked out the pieces of shell with her beak and let the egg fry to a crispy golden color. Now not only was the house clean, but food was ready for the

In the meantime the butter in the pan began to burn and the sparks caught the monkey's tail which was dangling close by.

monkey. She could go to the corner of the room and take a nap. The monkey saw all this with wonder and said to himself, "So this is how easy it is. I will stay home from tomorrow onwards and let her do the hard work."

The hen willingly agreed to go to work in the field again. As soon as she left the house the monkey went out to play. He played around in the forest for a good part of the day. He swung from tree to tree and picked fruits and nuts of his choice and enjoyed himself immensely. Finally he went into the house and tried to clean the floor just as the hen had done by flapping his arms, but that did not help at all. The dust rose up in the air and settled on the ground again. Frustrated, he abandoned the task of sweeping and tried to start the fire. Every time he blew into the embers his face was covered with ash. At last he had the fire going. He put the pan with some butter on the stove and climbed onto the beam above the hearth. He tried to lay an egg as the hen had done. He tried and tried but in vain and there was no egg. In the meantime the butter in the pan began to burn and sparks caught the monkey's tail which was dangling close by. The tail was on fire and he jumped down from the beam screaming and cursing the hen. He was sure that she had deliberately led him into this trap to hurt him.

Full of anger and pain, he could hardly wait for the hen to come home that evening. When she finally did come, quite unaware of the day's incidents, she was totally perplexed when the monkey began to attack her angrily. Crazed with anger the monkey would have killed her, had she not been able to escape through the open window. As she ran for her life she met a needle who asked her why she was in such a hurry. When she explained, the needle said, "Let me come with you. Two are better than one." So the hen and the needle went along together. They soon met a lump of salt who asked them where why were hurrying so. When they told him the reason he said, "Let me come with you. Three are better than two." The hen, the needle, and the salt went together and before long they met a stick. The stick too joined them, saying that four are better than three.

Together they went back to the house. The monkey had not yet come home. So they lay in wait to give him a nasty surprise. The needle hid in the crack of the floor, the salt in the ash in the hearth, the stick behind the door, and the hen on the beam above the hearth. Late in the evening the monkey came home chattering to himself. Not suspecting anything, he started to make a fire. As he blew into the cinders the salt burnt and sent out sparks into his face. Startled, the monkey sat down on the floor with a bang, only to be pricked by the needle in his fleshy rear. As he shrieked in pain the stick came out from its hiding place and continued the retribution by beating him up thoroughly. All this while the hen was excitedly dancing on the beam, cackling to herself: *"cote coco, cote coco*, he deserved it, he deserved it."* The monkey barely managed to run away but never returned to the house. So the four friends lived happily together.

Aming *Niwa*

Dangbo..o..o Dingbo..o..o.. a small group of houses stood on a mountainside. This was a quiet picturesque village that was surrounded by willow trees. Nearly everybody in the village owned some sheep but all the sheep were herded by a poor orphan girl. She was the village shepherd. Every day she would take them to the pastures near the blue pine forests where there was always ample grass and shade for the sheep. While the sheep grazed she would sit on a big rock and spin the wool. She would drop her spindle down from the rock and watch the long lengths of wool twirl and spin into a smooth thread. She never tired of watching this and every time she would try and drop the spindle further and further down to see how far she could get.

Every day, when the sun was directly overhead she would eat her lunch of *kaptang*, a flat circular bread made of buckwheat or wheat flour, and chili paste. When the sun began to sink towards the western mountain she would round up the sheep and guide them back to the village. She did this day after day and she had done it for as long as she could remember.

Now one day as usual she was sitting on the rock and spinning when she saw that the sun was directly overhead and she knew it was lunch time. So she began to unwrap the *kaptang* from the *torrath*, the cloth in which her lunch was packed, when the whole thing slipped out of her hands and rolled down the hill. The shepherd scrambled off the rock and ran after her *kaptang*. The packet rolled down the hill, bouncing off the boulders, dodging between the trees until it was nearly at the bottom of the hill. Just as she was about to get it, the packet fell into a mouse hole. She stood there

31

*She would drop her spindle down from the rock and watch the long lengths
of wool twirl and spin into a smooth thread*

quite helpless. Then she called out, "Aming Niwa, even if you eat the *kaptang*, please give me back the *torrath*."

"Why don't you come down?" came the prompt reply.

"How can I come down? The hole is too small."

"Just close your eyes and step right in" advised the mouse.

The shepherd closed her eyes and stepped into the mouse hole. Instantly she found herself in the home of the mouse. The mouse at once said, "Night is falling, why don't you sleep here tonight?"

The shepherd was surprised but agreed. The mouse then asked her what she would like for her supper. To this the shepherd replied, "I am a very poor girl, I can eat anything. Some leftovers would be fine for me."

But the mouse prepared her a sumptuous meal fit for a king. After the meal was over the mouse asked her, "How shall I prepare your bed?"

"I can sleep on some rags," said the shepherd.

The mouse made her a very comfortable bed. She slept that night on a *boden* with soft blankets and a pillow stuffed with the softest cotton. Before she went to bed the mouse warned her that there might be a lot of hustle and bustle in the night and she might actually feel her hair being touched but that she must try not to be disturbed. Indeed, there was much noise and movement in the mouse's house and she could feel little pulls and tugs on her hair throughout the night.

Next morning when she got up the mouse was already busy preparing her morning meal. After a hearty breakfast she was just about to leave when the mouse gave back her *torrath*, which was made into a packet.

"Don't unwrap the *torrath* until you reach home. Now close your eyes," said the mouse.

The shepherd took the *torrath* and closed her eyes. When she opened her eyes she was back in the pasture with her sheep. She felt her hair, and every strand of her hair was strung with a precious jewel, turquoise, *zis*, and corals. She ran home and opened the *torrath* and it was full of more jewels.

The rich girl in the village soon heard about the shepherd's lucky adventure and she asked her about it. The shepherd in her simplicity and kindness told her everything. The rich girl was filled with greed and she too wanted to get the jewels. So the next day she took the sheep to graze and did everything that the shepherd had done. But when the mouse asked her what she wanted for supper, the girl stated confidently, "I am a rich girl, and I am used to eating well, so I expect a very good supper." The mouse gave her some old *khuli*. The cold buckwheat pancakes were served with some even colder turnip *tsaoem*

When she was asked, "How shall I prepare your bed?" she replied, "I am a rich girl, I am used to sleeping very comfortably!" The mouse pulled some rags from a corner and gave them to the girl. So she had to sleep on some rags and cover herself with some more rags.

Before she went to bed the mouse cautioned, "Do not be disturbed by the noises in the house tonight. "

The girl thought she knew exactly what she was to expect. So when the noises started and there were little pulls and tugs at her hair she could hardly contain her excitement. As she peeked through her half-closed eyes she saw many mice around her and they started stringing things on her hair. The rich girl was extremely excited as she imagined all the jewels in her hair.

The following morning the mouse gave her back her *torrath* and told her to close her eyes. When she opened her eyes she was with the sheep. She felt her hair and every strand of her hair had been strung with mouse dung. She did not wait to go home but unwrapped the *torrath*. It was full of more dung, dried grasses, and mosses. The rich girl was fuming with anger as bitter tears of shame and humiliation stung her eyes. This was the price she had paid for her greed and condescension.

Acho La La

Dangbo..o..o Dingbo..o..o.. in a lone house on a hill top there dwelt a farmer with his wife and their daughter. The elderly couple were tired of farming their little patch of land which yielded so little. But more than that they had heard that there was a *sinpo* in the locality who was terrorizing everybody so that they had decided to run away and leave their daughter. One day the mother handed her daughter a roll of bamboo mat and said, "*Bomed*, spread out this bamboo mat and dry the barley in the sun. Tomorrow I shall grind some flour. Stay there and mind the grain."

When any grains are spread out to dry the pigeons and the ravens always take great risks just to steal a few . So the girl sat near the bamboo mat on which the grain had been spread out and waved a long bamboo stick about, calling "shoo shoo " to chase away the birds. While the girl was thus engaged the parents were busy making preparations to go away. Suddenly the girl noticed that a raven was sitting on the peach tree near the house and was cawing something to her with a tone of urgency. She listened and it said, "*Bomed* you stay, your father and mother are going away."

The girl jumped up and ran into the house. She was so relieved to see that her parents were still in the house. They had made a basket of *tsog*. "Lunch is not ready yet. We will call you for lunch. Go back to the barley before the birds finish it all." said the mother sternly. She went back and once again began chasing away the birds.

The raven went on cawing but she did not pay any attention to it until it began to dance excitedly and caw loudly and impatiently, "*Bomed*, you are alone, your parents have gone away!" This time

Just then she heard the sound, "tsahlahhk" as the chain was hurled down.

when the girl rushed into the house she was dismayed to see that they had indeed gone.

The girl was sad and lonely so she climbed up the peach tree to see if she could spot her parents in the distance. She looked in all directions but she could see nothing. She remained among the branches, frightened and tearful, when she suddenly heard a voice that said, "Whay, *Bomed*, throw me a peach."

Without realizing who the person was she plucked a big ripe peach and threw it to the stranger.

"*A khai*, that's fallen in the pig dung. Come down a few branches and throw me another," said the stranger.

The girl came down a few branches, again plucked another ripe peach and threw it to the person. Again the person said, "*A khai*, this one is gone into the cow dung. Come down and hand me a peach."

The girl innocently came down low enough to hand him a peach when the *sinpo* caught her hand and pulled her down. He then pushed her into the sack which he carried over his shoulders and took her to his house in *sinpoiyul*.

As they entered the *sinpo's* house the girl noticed a sickly old dog who feebly raised its head and looked at her. The dog had not been fed and it was starving. As she was passed by, it whispered, "Give me a mouthful of food and I will tell you three words of wisdom."

The girl took a piece of *tsog* which she still had in the folds of her *kira* and gave it to the dog who ate it gratefully and said, "Look into my ear and take out the three little packets. The seeds in each packet will be useful when you try to escape from the *sinpo*." The girl took the packet and put it in the folds of her *kira*.

The poor captive girl was not only very frightened but also extremely distressed for she knew that she would soon be eaten by the *sinpo*. One day the *sinpo* told her to pound some rice. As she pounded the rice the *sinpo* would call out to her and she had to answer his call, "Yes, I am here.". In this way he could be sure that she would not run away. With tears streaming down her cheeks and her head hung low in hopelessness she pounded rice despondently. A louse in her hair took pity on her and spoke to her. It said, "I will help you to run away from the *sinpo*."

"Who is that? " asked the girl, taken aback, for she had seen nobody in the house.

" It's me, a louse in your hair," whispered the diminutive voice.

"How can you help me?" asked the girl, at once filled with hope.

"You must take me out of you hair and place me on the mortar in a bit of your spittle. Then you must run away as quickly as you can."

The girl found the louse and pulled it out of her hair and placed it in a bit of her spittle and ran away.

Now every time the *sinpo* called the girl the louse replied saying, "Yes, I am here. I still have more rice to pound."

The *sinpo* did not realize that each time the voice of the louse was growing fainter. Finally all the spit dried up and the louse died. So when the *sinpo* heard no answer to his call he at once came to see what the matter was. On seeing that the girl had escaped he was indignant and began to pursue her right away. It was not long before the girl saw the *sinpo* in the distance following her. She ran as fast as she could but she knew that the *sinpo* would soon overtake her for he ran like the wind. She was quite desperate and did not know what to do for the *sinpo* was right behind her. Then she remembered the three seeds the dog had given her. She took the acorn pepper seed out and threw it towards the *sinpo*. In a trice a thick forest of pepper trees grew between her and the *sinpo*. The *sinpo* had to struggle through the forest and she could put some distance between her and her pursuer.

But it was not very long before the *sinpo* was close behind her, reaching out and trying to catch her, when she threw the pine seed. A thick forest of pines that grew close together kept the *sinpo* scrambling through the trees for a while but this neither thwarted nor exhausted him. He soon caught up with her and she threw down the last seed—and a huge field of bamboo sprung up. The bamboo stems were entwined like a net and the *sinpo* had to work very hard to get through this forest.

The hour was late and darkness was fast descending upon them. Soon the moon was rising, sending a faint glow all over the sky. The girl looked up towards the eastern hills and saw the full moon. She called out to him, "Acho La La, please save me from the *sinpo*. Send down your iron chain and not your woolen ladder."

Acho La La yawned prodigiously and said, "Wait a little. I am just rising."

"Please hurry, the *sinpo* will soon be here," pleaded the girl.

"Wait a bit, I'm just washing myself," said Acho La La, without a trace of haste in his voice.

"I can now see the *sinpo* has come very close, please throw your iron chain."

"Wait a little, I am just making my breakfast," said the moon.

The girl thought," This is hopeless," yet she implored the moon to hurry. But Acho La La was in no hurry at all.

"I am just eating my breakfast," announced the moon.

"Please, please hurry up," begged the girl.

"Wait a little, I am just putting away the dishes," said Acho La La, as if there was all the time in the world.

"The *sinpo* is here, hurry up, Acho La La!" cried the girl.

"Wait a little, I am just looking for the chain," said Acho La La as calmly as possible.

"I can feel the *sinpo's* breath, hurry up, please, please," cried the girl, now growing quite faint with fatigue and fear.

"Wait a little, I am just straightening out the chain," said Acho La La.

Now the girl could hardly speak "Please hurry," was all she could say. Just then she heard the sound, "tsahlahhk" as the chain was hurled down. With the last bit of her strength she climbed it as Acho La La began to pull up the chain. The girl could feel the tips of the *sinpo's* nails touch the soles of her feet as he stretched out his long arms to catch her.

On seeing what had happened the *sinpo* was totally incensed and he gruffly demanded that Acho La La[1] throw a chain for him too. But Acho La La went through the whole process of rising, washing, preparing breakfast and having it, and then finally looking for the chain. By this time the girl was safely in the moon. Acho La La finally threw down the woolen ladder which floated down flimsily, for it was made of wool. The *sinpo* impatiently seized it and began to climb it with incredible speed. When the *sinpo* was half-way up to the moon, Acho La La took out a huge knife, which was rather blunt and rusty from disuse and began to saw away at the woolen ladder for a long time until it broke and sent the sinpo plunging to the ground with a tremendous "Byaaaak". The impact of the fall was such that the *sinpo* went through the ground and was buried deep down in the earth. The girl decided to stay in the moon and look after the moon's cow. Today if you look carefully at the full moon, you might just be lucky enough to see the shape of the girl as she milks the moon's cow.

[1]   When somebody is very calm and slow in a situation that demands extreme urgency, it is said that the person is like Acho La La.)

The Tiger and the Frog

Dangbo..o..o Dingbo..o..o.. on the edge of the deep blue-green forests somewhere in central Bhutan, a frog was having a glorious time basking in the warm sun. He was sitting on the top of a large flat rock and looking at the world through his half-opened eyes. Suddenly a tiger came out of the forest and roared on seeing the frog. "What are you doing, brother frog?"

"I am sitting in the sun and enjoying it," answered the frog, quite startled by the sudden appearance of a tiger.

The tiger leaped on to the rock next to the frog and lay down. "I have been bothered by lice lately. Pick out the lice for me, brother frog," ordered the tiger. The frog quickly climbed onto the tiger's head and began to pick out the lice. The warm sun together with the soothing and rhythmic movement of the frog's fingers in his fur made the tiger sleepy and soon he was nodding off to sleep.

The frog was getting restless for the more he thought about the possibility of the tiger eating him the more nervous he got. The frog wondered what he could do to save himself. Eventually he had an idea which he thought might save him. He pretended to pick out the lice but he actually began to pull out the tiger's fur. He then stuffed the fur into his mouth and some into his rectum. When he was sure that there was enough fur to impress the tiger he began to question the tiger. "*Ashang* tiger, what do you eat?"

The tiger was still very sleepy and between his long and luxurious yawns he said, "I can eat many things...."

"Things like what?" interrupted the frog, trying not to sound to eager.

"Have a good look," insisted the frog, displaying his mouth with the tiger fur sticking out of it.

"When I am really hungry, I eat cattle, yaks, horses, and other big animals. Usually I am happy with a deer or pig or some other smaller animals. But when I am really hungry and cannot get anything else I have to eat very small animals like rabbits, squirrels and even frogs."

At this the frog had to hold his teeth from chattering and steady his shaking hands. Without much interest the tiger then asked, "What do you eat?"

The frog of course had been waiting for this question and immediately said, "Oh, I am a small animal so I usually eat the other smaller animals. But when I am really hungry I also like to eat something big like deer, cattle, and even tigers." At the mention of tigers, the tiger pricked up his ears with interest and asked, "Did you say tigers? You are joking, of course." The tiger then began to laugh.

The frog was pleased with the way the conversation was turning out and confidently went on, "In fact I had just eaten one before you came by. Look into my mouth."

The tiger suddenly sprang up and moved a few paces away and looked at the frog apprehensively.

"Have a good look," insisted the frog, displaying his mouth with tiger fur sticking out of it and his rectum which was also full of tiger fur. The tiger took one quick look and with a mighty leap jumped onto the land and disappeared into the forest.

As the tiger was leaping and springing through the forest a fox saw him and asked him what had happened. The tiger quickly told him. The fox laughed and said, " You have been tricked by a frog. Frogs don't eat anything bigger than a fly. Come, let's go back and see the frog."

"No, no," begged the tiger, backing away.

Pulling down a creeper from a nearby tree the fox said, "Look, if you are so afraid I'll tie this end of the creeper around my neck and you tie the other end around yours and we will go together."

Soon they were near the pond. The frog was still on the rock. As soon as he saw them coming he greeted them cheerfully, "Good, brother fox, I was just beginning to get hungry. I see that you have brought me a very special lunch." When the tiger heard this he sprang into the air and leapt like lightning through the forest. The fox, of course, could not keep up with the speed of the tiger and he was soon strangled to death. The tiger looked back at the fox, who had died with his mouth open and his teeth showing as if in a grin. "Stop grinning, you fool. You nearly succeeded in getting me eaten by the tiger-eating frog." The tiger was so afraid of the frog that he went to live in another forest as far away as possible from the frog.

The Shepherd

Dangbo..o..o Dingbo..o..o.. a young shepherd could be seen grazing his flock of sheep on the banks of a clear blue lake every day. He loved to sit and gaze at the lake to see the fish swishing about in the water, the animals that came to drink from it, or simply to watch the waves and the ripples that danced and played in an endless game. Everybody in the village whispered that nothing good would come of a boy who did nothing but laze around watching ripples on a lake.

One day while he was sitting on the banks of the lake he saw a white rat fighting a black rat. Fascinated he watched them for a long time. He could see that the black rat was much stronger and was about to kill the white rat. Being a compassionate man he picked up the white rat to save it from its enemy who was attacking it viciously. He held the gasping and beaten rat in his hand and blew on it gently. Then he dipped his finger into the lake and let the water from his finger drip into the mouth of the rat in an effort to revive it. Suddenly the water in the lake began to swirl and bubble in the most unusual way, and then it opened up and a woman came out of the lake. The beautiful and gracious woman smiled and said that she was a messenger from the underground world. She had been sent to get back the son of the subterranean king, who had carelessly ventured into the middle world disguised as a rat. She added that the subterranean king was pleased with the shepherd for saving his son and wanted to reward him. She then asked him to close his eyes and get on her shoulders. As they were going down through the water she said, "The king will offer you everything but you must insist on taking only the dog behind the door.

He was the Lu Throwa *or the Ferocious* Lu.

Everything from here is illusory once in your world. Only the dog is for real and will be of some use to you. Do not stay under the lake for more then three days or you will forget your human world."

As soon as the shepherd opened his eyes he found himself in a beautiful palace. The pillars were made of coral and the walls and the floors were made of turquoise and they shone like mirrors. There was feasting and music everywhere. Amidst the crowds of half-serpent half-human beings sat the *Luyi gyalpo*. He was the *Lu Throwa* or the Ferocious *Lu*. His angry and fierce face was encircled by a ring of serpents that seemed to lash out and dart their forked tongues threateningly. The enormous serpentine lower body thrashed and whipped about ominously. At the end of three days the shepherd asked the king to let him go. The king offered him bags of turquoise, but the shepherd refused. The king offered him gold and silver but he still refused. When the king asked, "What do you want that you refuse everything I offer?" the shepherd replied, "I would like to have only the dog behind your door!"

The king's face darkened and he said that he would not like to give away the dog. But the shepherd insisted that he wanted nothing else except the dog. Finally the king agreed saying, "Ya, Ya, if that's the only thing you want, take it. Be good to it and keep it clean."

The shepherd once again closed his eyes, this time with the dog tucked under his arm and he found himself on the banks of the lake. His sheep were still grazing around the lake. As it was close to sunset he rounded them up and took them home. As the dog sat in the corner of the kitchen looking at him with its head cocked to one side he began to wonder what it was that might be special about the dog because it did not look very different from any of the ordinary dogs. Perhaps the messenger had deceived him.

The following morning he took his sheep to graze on the meadows near the lake as usual. He kept the dog at home. When he brought the sheep home in the evening, he was pleasantly surprised to find that his house was swept and clean and there was fire in the stove and delicious food waiting for him. He wondered who had come to his house and done this for him. For several days this was repeated. Now he was really curious to see who was doing this for him. So he decided to hide and see. He pretended to go with his sheep as usual but he came back and hid behind the door. There was nobody in the house except his dog. As he watched, the dog took off the dog skin and a beautiful girl came out of it. The girl bathed in the stream and made offerings of milk towards the lake, chanting, "Offerings to my father, king of the subterranean world. King Tsuena Rinchen take my offering." She then set about to cleaning and sweeping the house and cooking the food. The shepherd at once jumped out from his hiding place, snatched up the dog skin and threw it into the fire. The girl saw what had happened and she said, "I am a nonhuman being and the skin was my protection from attracting too much attention. I am the daughter of the *Luyi gyalpo*. Now that you have prematurely destroyed my disguise you will face some trials and tribulation before we can live a normal life."

For many days the shepherd and his wife lived happily together. But one day the king of the region saw the girl. Instantly he saw that she was more beautiful than any of his five hundred wives and he wanted to marry her. So he called the shepherd and gave him an impossible task to perform, failing which the king would take his wife. The poor shepherd was extremely distraught because he was sure that he would not be able to do what he was asked to do. He went to his wife and told her.

"I will lose you to the king, because I will not be able to slash and burn all the trees on the mountainsides all by myself in one day," and he began to cry.

The girl said, "Do not worry. Perhaps the king of the lake can help us. Early tomorrow morning you go to the lake and ask the king of the *Lu* to loan you the sword box."

The next morning the shepherd went to the lake and shouted, "O, King Tsuena Rinchen, King of the *Lu*, please loan me your sword box for today." Suddenly a wave welled up from the bottom of the lake and splashed on the shore. When the water receded a tiny box was left on the shore of the lake. The girl then told her husband to take the box to the mountainside and open it. As soon as he had opened the box hundreds of swords came out of the box and slashed all the trees on the mountainside in a very short time.

The king said, "But that is not all. Now you must prepare the land for buckwheat cultivation within one day." This was an unachievable task that could never be done in a day's time! For it involved digging the ground, making the mounds, burning the turf, and spreading the mounds again.

The shepherd was once again in agony and went home to his wife and said that the king had given him an even more difficult task than the last one. The girl once again assured him that the king of the *Lu* could help him and he should not worry. So, instructed by his wife, the shepherd went to the shore of the lake and asked the king of the *Lu* for a loan of his hoe box. When the box was put on the shore of the lake in front of him he took it to where the mountainsides had been cleared on the previous day and opened it. As soon as he opened the box thousands of hoes came out and began preparing the land at an unbelievable speed and by midday the field was ready for sowing the seeds. The shepherd went to the king who gave him hundreds of measures of buckwheat which he quickly broadcast over the land. The shepherd was now sure that the king would be satisfied and not ask him to perform any more impossible tasks. He was mistaken. This time the king mocked, "Anyone can broadcast seeds, but if you really are so clever I want you to pick up all the seeds and bring them back to me. Every single seed."

At this the shepherd felt totally defeated because he thought now even the king of the Lu would not be able to help him. But his wife again assured him that her father could help him.

Full of anguish and apprehension the shepherd walked down to the lake and called, "King Tsuena Rinchen, King of the *Lu*, I have come to you once again to borrow the bird box."

Once again a wave welled up and splashed on the shore. When the wave receded the familiar box was on the shore. The shepherd took up the box and at once went towards the field. He put down the box and opened it, and out came thousands of birds twittering and fluttering about and within a short time all the buckwheat seeds were back in the bags. The shepherd took the bags to the king who became vehement.

"So, you are really very clever and you have done all the inconceivable tasks I have asked you to do. Now there is nothing more I can ask, except to declare war on you. We will meet tomorrow and see who is better. The winner will take the woman."

The shepherd's wife told him to borrow the people box this time. So he carried the people box and went in front of the king's army. As soon as the army came forward he opened the box. Hundreds of tiny men armed with swords, spears, bows and arrows came out of the box, hollering, "*Ga lo chap ni, ga sed ni* (Who shall we strike, who shall we kill?)." At this the shepherd said, "*Gyalpo seda, marmi go chap* (Kill the king and strike his army)." The little men killed the king and struck the army. With the king killed and his army defeated in the battle the shepherd did not have to worry about losing his wonderful wife and they lived in happiness, prosperity, and peace.

The Mother and the Ghost

Dangbo..o..o Dingbo..o..o.. there was a widow who lived with her only son. Soon after the son was born the father had died and she had brought up the child in the best way she knew how and taught him everything that she possibly could. Now he had grown into a strong young man and he looked after her very well but she was lonely and she often wished she could remarry.

The son was a hard-working conscientious young man who did all the work. One day while he was out in the forest collecting firewood he met a ghost. This hungry ghost with ash-gray skin and red gaping mouth looked at him through his dark eyes which had sunk into the depths of his sockets and hissed, "I am going to eat you." The boy who was not only strong but remarkably brave as well said, "How can you kill me without a fight? Let's have a fight tomorrow and if you win then you can kill me and eat me."

The ghost had to agree, for even ghosts have little power if they cannot evoke any fear in their victims. Fear in victims empowers spirits and ghosts, who then are capable of harm and destruction.

The next day the boy went to the forest at sunrise. He took his bow and his quiver full of arrows. The ghost did not come at the appointed time. They should have met in front of the big black boulder in the forest when the first rays of the sun touched the tops of the cypress trees on the hill. So the boy decided to lie in wait for the ghost. He hid behind a thick bush and waited. The ghost eventually came from the other direction, hoping to ambush the boy but instead he had a surprise waiting for him. As the ghost wandered around looking for the boy the latter shot his arrow right through the ghost's heart. He

The ghost wailed in pain as his body scalded and charred in the hot butter.

then chopped off the ghost's head and took it home and hung it in the corner of the roof as a warning for the other ghosts to keep away.

The boy warned his mother not to look at the head. But one day as the boy was out in the fields the mother happened to look up at the head. This was the chance that the ghost had been waiting for. Sobbing pathetically he begged her to listen to him. "Please listen to me. There has been a mistake. Your son mistook me for a ghost and killed me. Look at me, I am not a ghost. Please take me down and I will tell you something."

The mother was bewildered to see a head that could talk, but being rather foolish she took down the head and asked, "What do you have to tell me?" The ghost at once found out how foolish this woman was and decided that he could use her. "I am a very rich man. If you listen to me and do as I tell you my body will grow back in time and then I will marry you. Once you are my wife you will never have to do any work and you can have anything you want and you will never be lonely again. But first we must get rid of your son as he is very dangerous." This simple woman became quite excited at the prospect of marriage, for she had by now become preoccupied with the idea of remarriage! Easily convinced, she was ready to conspire with the ghost to get rid of her own son. "What must I do?" she asked, almost too eagerly.

The ghost then instructed her to take his head to the cave in the forest and feed him every day so that his body could grow back. The ghost said, "Now you must pretend to be sick and tell your son that only the milk of a lioness will cure you." The ghost was sure that the boy would be mauled and killed if he tried to get milk from a lioness, for wild animals with young are extremely protective and fiercely aggressive.

After she fed and put the head in the cave the mother took to her bed and began to moan and groan loudly until her son came to her side. Full of concern he asked her how he could help her. Just as the ghost had told her, she asked him to get her the milk of a lioness.

In sincere eagerness to help his ailing mother the son sought out a lioness with cubs. He lured one of the cubs and killed and skinned it. He put on the skin over himself and suckled with the other cubs and filled a small container which he held, concealed under the skin. He took the milk to the mother but she still did not recover. She continued to moan and groan, saying, "This illness is more serious than I had thought. The medicine was not right."

Now the ghost was fearful, for this boy was surely an extraordinary man. So he spoke to the woman and he asked her to send the son to the land of the demons where he would definitely be killed. So one day the mother called her son to her side and said, "Aye, my son, you have been good to me, but only one thing will make me better. I need the all-curing medicine. This medicine is only found in the fruit that grows in the land of the demons."

The son replied, "I will do anything if there is a way to cure you." He then set off for the land of the demons.

The boy ventured into the unknown for many days. He climbed nine mountains and crossed nine valleys, numerous gorges and ravines before he reached the land of the demons. He went into the house of the demons and hid in the attic of the house. He watched the demons and he saw that they ate the fruit from a particular tree every day. The fruit tree was in the middle of the lake but they did not go to pluck the fruit themselves. They sent their maid, who was a beautiful human girl. The girl was in a state of perpetual slumber for the demons whipped her every morning with a golden whip and put her to sleep. So this beautiful girl lay sleeping peacefully for the whole day. When they came home in the evening and wanted more fruit they whipped her with the silver whip and this roused her out of her deep slumber and she did their bidding. She would then sit in a big golden frying pan which flew across the lake. She then plucked some of the fruit and flew back in the frying pan, bringing with her the sustenance for her obnoxious masters.

The boy waited until the demons had all left the house to go to their various works of destruction. He then came out of his hiding place. He took up the silver whip and whipped the girl. She woke up from her deep deep slumber. She was amazed to see a human being and asked, "Who are you and where are you from?"

The boy told her who he was and asked her to help him. The girl readily agreed for she had been waiting for an opportunity to escape from her monstrous masters. "But we must hurry because the demons will come home soon," she cautioned.

Then the two of them sat in the golden pan and crossed the lake. The tree was guarded by snakes, and when they sensed the presence of an intruder in the pan they began to attack them. With gaping mouths exposing their lethal fangs, these monsters raised up their heads and darted at them aggressively. But the boy was a skillful archer and he began to down them one by one. In the meantime the girl plucked the ripe juicy fruits from the tree, hoping that at least one of them would be the health-restoring fruit. As the last snake writhed in pain and died there was a sinister rumble as the demons realized what had happened. But it was too late, for the golden pan was already high up in the air flying with the speed of the wind.

The magical pan flew quickly across valleys and over the mountains and soon they were in the house of the boy. Having eaten all the fruits the mother could no longer pretend to be sick.

No longer burdened with an ailing mother the boy resumed his work in the fields while the girl stayed home to help the mother with the housework.

The mother was always a little hostile and very secretive, and the girl grew uneasy and suspicious. One day she saw the mother secretly preparing a bundle of food. She watched and followed her as she began to head towards the forest. The mother went into a cave and soon she heard her talking to someone. She tiptoed to the entrance of the cave and peered in cautiously. She was appalled on seeing that the mother was feeding an ash-colored man with bloodshot eyes and hair that stood on end like the quills on an agitated porcupine. "This is a ghost," thought the girl, shivering all over. As she strained her ears to listen to their conversation, she heard the ghost say, "Now we have tried to kill the boy and we have failed. The surest way to get rid of him is to poison him."

"I know my son likes to drink *ara*. I will give him some poisoned *ara* this evening," offered the foolish mother.

The girl could hardly wait for the boy to come home that evening. Having told him all that she had seen and heard she added, "And they plan to poison you this evening." The boy was shocked and bitterly hurt when he realized that his own mother had contrived with the ghost to kill him. But he was no fool and he knew that he had to defend himself. So he began to plan his counterattack. He found a *zang* and filled it with butter and let it boil on the stove, then he fitted it with a wick, as in a butter lamp, and waited for his mother. Soon the mother came in carrying a *palang*, the cylindrical bamboo container for spirituous liquors. "Here son, you must be tired. Have some delicious *ara* I distilled especially for you," said the mother as she poured out a cup of *ara* and held it out to her son.

The boy took the *ara* and pretended to drink it but actually poured it down his chin into his *gho*. Then he lit the wick in the butter for he knew that his mother had told the ghost to come into the house when she lit the butter lamp. The ghost, on seeing the light, rushed into the house, "Is he dead already? Now I can eat your meat and drink your hot blood to celebrate your son's death!"

The poor foolish woman stood there stunned, only realizing now what she had done while the boy jumped onto the ghost and threw him into the boiling butter. The ghost wailed in pain as his body scalded and charred in the hot butter.

The remains of the ghost were buried in a deep hole that was dug at the cross roads, for it is believed that the power of the people who pass over the ghost will further suppress and subdue its powers. A black chorten was built over it.

As for the mother, who was now filled with remorse and shame, she cried and begged for mercy. The boy was truly a good man and he forgave her but he made her seek a *tsawa lama* and spend the rest of her days in prayer and meditation.

The boy then married the girl who had escaped with him from the demons and lived happily together for many years.

Bum Dolay Penzom and
Bo Serba Tung Tung

Dangbo..o..o Dingbo..o..o.. somewhere among the valleys amidst the rugged mountains of Bhutan, there lived a poor farmer with her only son, *Bo* Serba Tung Tung, who used to herd the cattle every day on the mountainsides. These mountainsides were common grazing grounds and many other herders grazed their cattle there too. *Bum* Dolay Penzom, who was the only daughter of the richest family in the village, also brought her cattle to the pastures. As the cattle grazed the young herders would spend their time playing all sorts of games, telling stories or singing songs together. In the course of time *Bo* Serba Tung Tung fell in love with *Bum* Dolay Penzom. In the beginning their courtship had been confined to merely teasing or singing *tsangmo* to each other across the valleys. As time progressed their *tsangmo* had grown into *Bold* and passionate love songs. Now, the otherwise quiet and shy girl always made sure that she was not very far from where *Bo* Serba Tung Tung was grazing his cattle. They were in love with each other and they were happy to spend many days together. They kept their love secret because they knew that their relationship would not be approved by their families, for *Bo* Serba Tung Tung was a poor widow's son while *Bum* Dolay Penzom's family was rich and commanded respect throughout the village.

Soon *Bum* Dolay Penzom was expecting *Bo* Serba Tung Tung's child. She tried to conceal her pregnancy by wearing two thick *kiras* together carelessly and tied loosely around her waist with a big *kaira*. But as she grew heavy with the child her methods of concealment failed and one day the mother found out. Everyone

As time progressed their tsangmo *had grown into bold and passionate love songs.*

was outraged. "What shame you have brought upon this family," they all accused *Bum* Dolay Penzom.

Bum Dolay Penzom's brother was a cruel and arrogant man and he felt that it was his duty to avenge this humiliation. He began to devise and plot the murder of his sister's lover. One day he said to his sister, "Today I shall herd the cows, you take a rest." *Bum* Dolay Penzom had a premonition that something terrible would be done to her lover so she alerted him to keep away from her brother. *Bum* Dolay Penzom's brother had resolved to kill *Bo* Serba Tung Tung at all costs.

Bo Serba Tung Tung knew he was in danger but he did not know the extent of the danger. One morning when he arrived at the pasture with his cattle, *Bum* Dolay Penzom's brother who had been lying in wait for him suddenly attacked him and stabbed him several times with his dagger.

When the brother came home in the evening with a smug grin on his face, *Bum* Dolay Penzom knew that he had done something terrible. She rushed to her lover's house and found him lying in bed, mortally wounded. Henceforth she went secretly to nurse him every day. When he was a little better she gave him a black scarf and a white scarf and said, "When you feel better, hang the white scarf out of your window so that I will know that you are feeling better. Hang out the black scarf if you feel worse. Although I cannot be with you I can at least know how you are."

Every day *Bum* Dolay Penzom looked anxiously at his window. She was always relieved to see the white scarf at his window for then she knew that he was recovering well. One woeful day the black scarf hung ominously from the window and without a thought she ran to his house. She was overcome with grief when she reached the house and found out that he had died; in spirit *Bum* Dolay Penzom too died with her lover. From then on she went around dazed, not able to differentiate between day and night.

As the funeral preparations were being made she too prepared to go to his funeral. While others fried *tsog*, and distilled *ara*, she filled a *bamairuchung* or a *mithan* horn with mustard oil and ground a bag of chili powder. On the day of the funeral *Bum* Dolay Penzom stood aside from the crowds, gazing fixedly at the pyre. When the smoke and flames from the funeral pyre rose high into the sky, she knew it was time for her to go too. Taking handfuls of the chili powder she scattered them in the air. The fine powder drifted in the wind and got into the people's eyes and noses. All the mourners and the *choepas* alike began to sneeze, wheeze, and cry. While the people nursed their smarting eyes and noses she doused herself in the mustard oil and jumped onto the pyre. The blazing flames quickly engulfed her Body and she too disappeared from this world. When the people could finally see they realized what had happened. But it was too late.

As the village slowly recovered from the shock of the unfortunate happenings two banana saplings grew on the spot of the cremation site. *Bum* Dolay Penzom's brother saw that and, realizing that his sister and her lover were reBorn in the form of these saplings, he promptly uprooted them. The lovers then took on a series of rebirths and deaths. Their time together was always troubled and short. Their karma was still not cleansed enough, as we say in Bhutanese. They were the victims of a force stronger than themselves, they had to travel the entire path set by destiny. They were reBorn as a male and a female cat but a dog killed the male. Then as a rooster and a hen, but the hen was eaten by a fox. Then they were reBorn as a bull and a cow. The young bull was sold by the owner to someone far away and they never met again. It was only after several more births and deaths that they were finally reBorn again in the human form. As fate would have it, the lovers were Born far away from each other without any knowledge of each other's existence.

Bum Dolay Penzom was Born as the daughter of a rich family while *Bo* Serba Tung Tung was Born as the son of a poor potter. *Bo* Serba Tung Tung became a potter and went aBout the business of turning pots and selling his products from door to door. In the meantime *Bum* Dolay Penzom lived a leisurely life befitting the daughter of a rich family but deep inside she felt a sadness she could not understand. One day, as usual, the potter filled a basket with his pots and started on his rounds. During the course of his day he happened to stop at the rich house of *Bum* Dolay Penzom to try and sell his remaining pots. On seeing the potter, *Bum* Dolay Penzom came out of the house to buy some pots. As she was selecting the pots and negotiating the price, she suddenly had a vivid recollection of her lover and the various lives they had lived together. She was so overcome with excitement that she swooned and fell to the ground.

Bum Dolay Penzom's mother was alarmed on seeing what had happened and believing the potter to be responsible, she berated and chased him away saying, "You, dirty beggar. Look what you have done to my daughter. Now go away quickly before I set the dogs after you." The poor potter was completely astonished, but he quickly gathered up his pots and went his way not even daring to cast a backward glance.

After a while *Bum* Dolay Penzom regained consciousness and she immediately asked for the potter. Her mother explained that the potter had been scolded and chased away because he had made her unconscious. To everyBody's amazement, without saying a word to anyone, *Bum* Dolay Penzom at once began to follow him.

When she finally caught up with him she told him of their past lives and asked, "Don't you remember anything? I used to be *Bum* Dolay Penzom and you were *Bo* Serba Tung Tung."

At this revelation *Bo* Serba Tung Tung was so overwhelmed with shock and gratitude that he too fainted. At last, they were free. Their fate had freed them to live together, and their love had prevailed.

Ashi Dunglidolma waited outside the gate.

Ashi Dunglidolma

Dangbo..o..o Dingbo..o..o.. there was a king who had three daughters. They were called *ashi* Yulidolma, or princess Turquoise Tara, *ashi* Sarlidolma or princess Golden Tara, and *ashi* Dunglidolma or princess Copper Tara. Each *ashi* was as beautiful as the others. The fame of their beauty and the wealth of their father's kingdom had reached far and wide. There were many suitors who wished to marry them. The *ashis* were well aware of all their suitors but each of them secretly wanted to marry only *sai* Jangchu Dorji, a prince of the northern kingdom, for he was said to be not only the wealthiest but also the handsomest and the kindest and the gentlest of all the suitors.

Sai or prince Jangchu Dorji also wanted to marry one of the princesses but he wanted to find out which of them was the kindest and the humblest. He therefore disguised himself as a beggar and stood at the gates of the princesses' palace, begging to be employed in the palace. When the king saw him he took pity on the poor beggar and made him the cowherd. Now, it was the custom that every day the *ashis* took turns to help to herd and milk the cows. So on the first day it was *ashi* Yulidolma who came to do the milking. It had rained during the night and it was muddy everywhere, so *ashi* Yulidolma told the cowherd to kneel down in the mud so that she could sit on his back while she milked the cows. In this way she did not dirty herself. *Sai* Jangchu Dorji did as he was told. When all the cows had been milked *ashi* Yulidolma made a symbolic offering of the milk to the gods and deities then to each of the kings of the four directions. Finally she secretly made an offering to *sai* Jangchu Dorji, sprinkling some milk in the air, saying, "*Choy choyshi Sai Jangchu Dorji shayla stuchu shi* (I make this offering, may it be pleasing to prince Jangchu Dorji)". The milk that she sprinkled fell into the cowherd's mouth. *Sai* Jangchu Dorji professed surprise and said, "*Ashi*, the milk you offered to *sai* Jangchu Dorji has come into my mouth. What should I do with it? Shall I swallow it or spit it out?"

"Spit it out," was the scornful answer.

"The rich milk has made me thirsty, *ashi* Yulidolma. Please let me drink a cupful," begged *sai* Jangchu Dorji.

"I will not waste milk on a dirty beggar," was the reply.

Soon it was lunch time, and *ashi* Yulidolma sat on a high rock and ate her rice and meats and let Jangchu Dorji sit far away from her and eat his poor meal of **kuli** and chili paste.

As the midday sun got hot *ashi* Yulidolma fell asleep in the shade of a tree. *Sai* Jangchu Dorji watched her. Although she was unkind and rude he had to be sure whether they were destined to be together. So he took a turquoise ring off his finger and tossed it into the air singing, "*Ashi Yulidolma, Yuyi zokey thee, tse gang thendi yodna ashi cha la zu shu, tse gang thendi med na boko na la log sho.*(Princess Turquoise Tara, this turquoise ring I offer. If we are to share a common fate, may it fall in your hands. If not then let it come to me)." The turquoise ring fell into his own lap.

Ashi woke up and chided him, "What was that you were mumbling about?"

"Even a beggar has songs for his joys and songs for his sorrows," came the quick reply.

As dusk fell and it was time to go home, *sai* Jangchu Dorji gathered the cattle and turned them homewards. *Ashi* Yulidolma made him carry her across the river because she did not want to get wet. So he carried the *ashi* on his back. With his left hand he held the *ashi's* legs behind his back and with his other hand he held the stick with which he drove the cattle home. The *ashi* was repulsed at having to touch a beggar but she had to hang onto him tightly.

On the second day it was the second princess Sarlidolma's turn to milk the cows and she was just like her older sister. Sai Jangchu Dorji knew that his fate was not tied with either *ashi* Yulidolma or *ashi* Sarlidolma.

On the third day it was the youngest princess *ashi* Dunglidolma's turn. As on the other days the place was wet and muddy and *sai* Jangchu Dorji offered to kneel down so that she could sit on him and milk the cows. But she was shocked and refused saying, "No, no, I will not do such a thing."

When she made the offerings and *sai* Jangchu Dorji 's share fell into his mouth he asked, "*Ashi* Dunglidolma, what should I do? Your offering to *sai* Jangchu Dorji has fallen into my mouth. Shall I swallow it or spit it out."

"If it has fallen into your mouth it must be for a good reason. Swallow it by all means."

Then when he asked for a cup of milk to drink she said, "Drink all you can. There is enough milk for you to drink."

During lunch time she insisted that they sit together and share their meals. After their lunch, like her sisters *ashi* Dunglidolma also fell asleep in the shade of a tree. *Sai* Jangchu Dorji sat by her side and watched her. Then he took off his copper ring and as on the previous days, tossed it in the air, singing, "*Ashi Dunglidolma, dungi zokey thee, tse gang thendi yodna ashi cha la zu shu, tse gang thendi med na boko na la log sho* (Princess Copper Tara, this copper ring I offer. If we are to share a common fate, may it fall into your hand. If not let it return to me)." When the *ashi* woke up she was surprised to find a ring around her finger. *Sai* Jangchu Dorji of course denied any knowledge of it when she questioned him. "Perhaps it's a good omen," she thought to herself and decided to keep it on.

Then she asked him what he was singing and he replied, saying, "Even a beggar has his songs for his joys and songs for his sorrows," but this was all he would say.

When they returned home in the evening *sai* Jangchu Dorji offered to carry her across the river but she said she preferred to hold his hand and cross the river. By the end of the third day *sai* Jangchu Dorji knew which princess he wanted to marry. But he had to be absolutely sure that *ashi* Dunglidolma was truly the right wife for him, so he had to test her further.

The king now decided that it was time for his daughters to get married so he invited all the suitors to come and seek their brides. He decreed that each of the suitors would have to perform a heroic feat before he could qualify to marry any of his daughters. The suitors came from the four directions and they performed wondrous and heroic feats. On the appointed day the suitors presented themselves bearing the testimonies of their feats. One of them had dragged a dragon out of the skies, its body still steaming with moisture while spitting out flames of fire. Another had tamed a *chuzin* or a sea serpent and now it slithered and crawled behind its master. The third one led the leader of the *sinpos* on a leash of thick leather after he had subdued the *sinpos* in the region.

The day before the ceremony at which each of the three princesses had to present a scarf to the prince of her choice, *sai* Jangchu Dorji took a new-born puppy and put it into *ashi* Dunglidolma's bed. Then he woke her up and said, "You have just given birth to this freak. Now if you don't choose me for your husband I shall tell everybody about this."

The *ashi* had no choice but to agree. The next day as the first rays of the sun touched the palace rooftops the ceremony took place. Everybody was very pleased as *ashi* Yulidolma confidently walked up to the Eastern King and presented her scarf to him. *Ashi* Sarlidoma presented her scarf to the Western King. Poor *ashi* Dunglidolma held down her head and demurely handed her scarf to the poor and dirty man standing in the crowd. Everybody was shocked and repulsed! The king was so angry and humiliated that he immediately banished them from his kingdom.

Sai Jangchu Dorji and *ashi* Dunglidolma traveled for many days. They crossed many valleys and climbed many mountains. One day they reached a big herd of cattle. *Ashi* Dunglidolma said, "I wonder whose cattle these are. Would it not be pleasant if we were the owners?"

"Perhaps it would, " came the languid reply.

Then he said that he would go to the herders' camp to beg for some food. When he came back he brought hot and delicious food, saying how kind the herders were.

For the next few days they passed through fields of barley, wheat, and mustard and large herds of horses, sheep, and goats. Each time *sai* Jangchu Dorji would bring his wife good food from the kind herders. In fact all the animals belonged to him and his herders naturally gave the best to their prince. One day they reached a beautiful big dzong situated in a broad valley beside a silvery river that meandered through the entire valley. It was exquisitely beautiful. *Ashi* Dunglidolma thought, "This palace is even more grand than my father's and the place more beautiful."

Sai Jangchu Dorji as usual went into the *dzong* to beg for some food and *ashi* Dunglidolma waited outside the gate. As she waited for her husband she began talking to a man who said he was the sweeper of the palace. When she asked him who owned the *dzong*, the sweeper was surprised. "Don't you know? This is *sai* Jangchu Dorji 's palace."

Then *ashi* Dunglidolma asked, "Is *sai* Jangchu Dorji in his palace?"

"Did you not see him?" retorted the sweeper, even more surprised. "He just went into the *dzong* dressed as a beggar."

Before *ashi* Dunglidolma could say anything more *sai* Jangchu Dorji came out of the gates and welcomed her to his palace. Then he explained to her that he had had to put her through the test because he wanted to be very sure that they were indeed destined to be king and queen. He added, "I wanted a queen who is kind and humble and you are truly the right queen for me."

What followed in the next few days were lavish feasts and celebrations to commemorate the marriage of *sai* Jangchu Dorji to *ashi* Dunglidolma. Soon the news of the wedding was heard far and wide. When *ashi* Sarlidolma and *ashi* Yulidolma heard about it they came to extend their good wishes to the newly wed royal couple while their father, filled with remorse and shame, came to beg forgiveness for his ill treatment of them. *Sai* Jangchu Dorji and *ashi* Dunglidolma not only forgave him but showered him with precious gifts.

After an emotional and tearful parting the princess and her husbands crossed many valleys and climbed many mountains.

The Princess with Three Breasts

Dangbo..o..o Dingbo..o..o.. there were a king and a queen who were getting old and they worried a great deal because they had no children. Their agony suddenly came to an end one day when, way past her childbearing days, the queen rejoiced on realizing that she was pregnant with their first child. The birth of the daughter was celebrated with feasts and festivals throughout the kingdom. But when the royal astrologer was summoned to come and make the princess's horoscope a sudden uneasiness fell upon the kingdom as he gloomily warned the royal couple, "The princess has three breasts and the significance of this is very bad for the country. It is said in the books that the day such a freak appears there will be deaths, famines and other catastrophes. We must get rid of the princess."

"There must be some remedy," exclaimed the king and queen in disbelief. How could fate be so cruel? They had had to wait so long for a child and when the child finally came along they had to get rid of her. They were grief stricken.

Time passed quickly and the princess grew into a beautiful girl. But there was no way of remedying the significance of the third breast. Every day the king's ministers and especially the royal astrologer reminded him about the ill omen of the third breast. The king would sit and think of ways to save his daughter from being killed. Then suddenly he had a plan. He issued a royal proclamation which said that anyone who would marry his daughter and leave the country would get half his wealth. Nobody dared to come forward and days passed. Then one day two men stood at the palace gate. "We will marry the princess," they announced.

What a blow it was for the royal parents to see their daughter's suitors, for one of them was blind and he was being led by a hunchback! The king knew that this was his last chance to save his daughter so he agreed to let her go. He gave them jewels, gold, silver, cattle, and grains and told them to go as far away as possible from the kingdom.

After an emotional and tearful parting the princess and her husbands crossed many valleys and climbed many mountains before they finally settled down in a valley. They lived together for many days and were quite happy. Both the men were very fond of their wife. But it so happened that the hunchback grew jealous of the princess's affections for the blind man and he contrived to get rid of him. One day he brought some meat and said, "Here's some meat I got for you. Fry it and eat it. "

The blind man gratefully accepted the gift and right away set to fry it. But being blind he accidentally dropped some water in the pan in which the meat was already sizzling in the hot oil. The oil sputtered into to his face. The pain was agonizing, as it stung and burned. He covered his face and ran for water. After splashing water repeatedly on his face the stinging and the burning subsided but his eyes hurt and tears ran out of them uncontrollably. Eventually when he felt sure that his eyes would fall out a strange thing happened. The pain gradually subsided and he saw light, then objects became recognizable. He saw the stove, the fire, the pots and pans. He could see! What was this magic that had cured him? He looked into the frying pan and was appalled, for the meat in front of him was from a poisonous snake, he recognized it for he had seen snakes before he became sightless after a long illness. The friend had not even bothered to skin it, for a blind man would never see it. The meat which was to poison him had cured him. How strangely fate worked!

Gradually bitter resentment and anger swelled in his heart as he realized that his friend had intended to kill him. What should he do now? Before he could think further he heard the hunchback and the princess coming into the house. Impulsively he hid behind the door, thinking, "What should I do?" The next moment he sprang out, caught the princess and picked her up and threw her at the hunchback, shouting, "You two wanted to kill me, but you see I don't die so easily!"

The princess crashed against the hunchback and both fell to the floor. They rose slowly from the ground in total shock staring at the blind man, who now looked at them boldly. In silence they stood together and faced each other for they realized that great miraculous changes had taken place in them. The impact of the princess's body crushing against the hunchback had straightened his body while the same impact had burst her third breast. They stood there staring at each other perplexed and confused, feeling and studying their own bodies for a long time. Eventually they realized, as if waking from a long dream, that they were each free of their handicaps.

It was the strange and incomprehensible twist of fate that they had been born to suffer their own agonies and then had been brought together through unusual circumstances to help each other to find freedom from the physical bondages which had so far ruled their lives.

For the drum was a molam gang tab nga *or a wish-granting drum.*

The Adventures of the Poor Boy

Dangbo..o..o Dingbo..o..o.. there was a boy who had neither parents nor a home. So he was free to travel and seek out adventures as he pleased. A life of travel and adventure had made him alert and prudent. Armed only with his wits and discernment the poor boy would walk from village to village and he always found enough food to eat and a warm shelter wherever he went.

One day while he was crossing a huge open field he saw two young men who were engaged in an intense tug of war over a piece of cloth. As he drew nearer to them he recognized the object of their contention to be not a simple piece of cloth but a ragged cap. Rather amused, he asked them why they were fighting over an old worthless cap. They explained, "This is no ordinary cap. It is the *dipshing moguli*. The wearer of this cap can become invisible."

The boy immediately wanted to have the cap and he had an idea. He said, "Listen here, I can help you. As neither of you trusts the other I will hold the cap and stand here. You two go down to the end of the field and when I count three you race back to me. Whoever gets here first shall keep the cap."

The men thought that this was a good idea and willingly agreed. As soon as their backs were turned the poor boy put on the cap and disappeared with it.

With this wondrous object now in his possession he did not have to plan how he would get every meal as he used to do in the past. Whenever he grew hungry or thirsty he simply put on his cap and helped himself to the food and drink of his choice.

The carefree life became even more appealing and he continued to travel widely throughout the mountain ranges and the abundant valleys of Bhutan. During one of his travels he chanced to come upon two old men who were pushing and shoving each other violently. But both of them clutched the sides of a wooden bowl. The bowl was old and worn out, the *sey* or lacquer polish was all but completely gone, and the bare wood showed through. The poor boy watched them and thought, "I wonder what is so special about the old bowl. But if two grown up people can fight so intensely over it must be worth something." He went over to them and asked them why they were fighting over an old bowl. They told him that this was no ordinary old bowl. It was a *zsa shong dem shong* bowl and it could produce any kind of food any time the owner asked for it. The poor boy again suggested that he hold the bowl while they go to a distance and run back to him and he would then give it back to the person who reached him first. The men thought that this was a good idea and agreed immediately for they were both tired of fighting the tedious battle. But the moment he got the bowl he put it into his *gho* and put on the *dibshing moguli* and became invisible. In the same way he also acquired a *nga* or a large drum used during religious rites and rituals that he could ride on. For the drum was a *molam gang tab nga* or a wish-granting drum. With these three very precious things the poor boy traveled effortlessly, ate well, and had everything that he desired. Now his life was easy and the challenge that motivated his rovings was gone and he decided to settle down to the conventions of a normal life, at least for a while.

He married a poor girl and lived with her in her house. He did not tell her about the three precious objects he had but he provided her with everything that she required for them to live comfortably. After some years he became restless and decided to go and meditate. He chose a small cave in a cluster of white rocks in a lake, which was far away from all settlements. The only way to get to the cave was by crossing the lake. The poor boy blindfolded the girl eyes and made her ride on the drum with him across the lake.

The couple lived and meditated in the cave for many days. But now the girl grew suspicious and wondered how her husband could produce food without lighting a fire and travel without having to walk. She cajoled and coaxed him to tell her about his magical powers. He trusted her fully now and told her about the drum and the bowl but he did not tell her about the cap. Years passed by and the girl became intensely lonely and she missed her parents very much and longed to see them. So she decided to run away. She stole the drum and the bowl and flew across the lake. The poor boy was bitterly angry but also totally helpless when he found out that she had not only run away but also stolen his possessions! There was no food for him and he was very hungry and could no longer meditate for his stomach growled and his head felt dizzy for want of food. He went in search of food but he could find nothing for the rocks were bare and devoid of any vegetation.

Then one day as he sat in his cave some food crumbs fell from above him. He picked up the food and ate it. On investigation, he found out that there was a nest of garudas at the top of his cave and the food he got was what had dropped while the mother fed the chicks. The garuda mother would fly across the lake and bring food to her chicks. Now he was completely dependent upon the garudas. One day he saw a vicious snake that had crawled up the rocks and begun to attack the chicks. Although garudas are actually supposed to kill snakes the helpless young chicks were no match for their adversary. The poor boy quickly put on his cap, became invisible, and killed the snake. On finding out how the meditator had saved the chicks the father and mother garuda were grateful to him and asked him what they could do for him. This was his only chance so he said, "I wish to be taken across the lake to the other side." The garuda couple joined their powerful wings together and carried him across the lake.

He did not go to his wife's house right away. He wanted some time to think. So he wandered around as he used to do in the earlier days until one day he saw a most intriguing sight. He was sitting near a solitary *tsamkhang* or hermitage when he saw a *tsampa* or meditator come out of the hut. The *tsampa* went towards a gigantic cypress tree. Around the tree there were some flowering plants. The *tsampa* plucked a yellow flower and caressed his body with it. Instantly he was transformed into a monkey who climbed up the trees and fed on the fruits and nuts. The boy was completely awestruck and watched patiently and attentively. After the monkey had eaten enough he came back to the tree and plucked a white flower with which he caressed his body. The monkey was transformed into the *tsampa* and went into the hut to resume his meditation. The boy went to the tree and plucked one yellow flower and one white flower and headed towards his wife's home with a smile on his face for now he had a way to punish her for her dishonesty.

Once near her house he put on his magical cap and waited for her to come. Just as she was stepping over the threshold of her house he touched her upper body with the flower and watched her change into a monkey. The mother and father screamed in shock and dread and fell into a state of panic on seeing their daughter who was now half-human and half-monkey. The poor boy took off his cap and walked into the house, pretending that he was unaware of anything. As he was dressed like a *gomchen* they immediately begged him, "We are so glad you have come, *Lopon Gomchen*. Please do some divinations. Something terrible has happened to our daughter."

Feigning concern and sympathy, he solemnly held his prayer beads to his forehead and proceeded to do some divinations and said, "All this has happened because you have things that do not belong to you. You have some stolen goods in the house. Is this true?"

"It's true, true," they confessed and hastened to bring out the bowl and the drum. They asked him to give them to the meditator who lived on the white rocks. He agreed to do so. Then the girl was brought in and he rubbed the white flower on her and she was instantly transformed to her original self. Before the girl could regain herself completely and recognize her husband, the holy *gomchen* had already turned his back and was leaving the house with the three precious objects.

But she was soom confronted by a big surly leopard who roared, "Whay, Bomed, I am going to eat you.

Mekhay Doma

Dangbo..o..o Dingbo..o..o.. there was a young girl called Mekhay Doma who had to carry food provisions to her parents who were meditating far away in the mountains. Their *tsamkhang* or hermitage was a long way from home but the girl did not mind the journey. Her parents were aged and could no longer work on their little farm so they had decided to spend the rest of their lives in prayer and meditation. Every month she would prepare a huge load of flour, butter, tea, and vegetables. Bent almost double under this heavy load she would struggle up the mountainside, for this was just one way of fulfilling her *dinlam* or repaying her parents for what they had done for her. The forest on the mountain was full of wild animals. Some of the animals had watched this girl with interest for several months now. One day they positioned themselves along her usual path and waited for her.

As she trudged up the mountainside carrying her heavy load she first met a wild boar who greeted her, then grunted and said, "Whay, **Bomed**, I am going to eat you."

"No, no, not now. Look at me. My skin is stuck to my bones. I am thin and full of sinews. When I come back from my parents I'll be fat and tasty. Then you can eat me," pleaded Mekhay Doma.

The boar grunted once more, looked at her skeptically and then agreed, "Ya, ya."

So Mekhay Doma walked on until she met a monkey who came by, chattering and screeching wildly in front of her. "Whay, **Bomed**, I want to eat you," he said as he hung upside down from a branch, all the time scratching himself.

Once again the girl replied, "No, no, not yet. Look at me. My skin is stuck to my bones. I am thin and full of sinews. You can eat me when I come back from my parents. At that time I'll be fat and tasty."

The monkey too agreed and swung through the trees screeching and chattering as he went.

Then Mekhay Doma walked on quickly, hoping that this was the last animal she would meet before she reached her parents' *tsamkhang*. But she was soon confronted by a big surly leopard who roared, "Whay, *Bomed*, I am going to eat you."

"No, no, not yet. Look at me. My skin is stuck to my bones. Eat me when I come back from my parents. I'll be fat and tasty by then," pleaded Mekhay Doma.

The leopard walked past her. Then he cocked his head to one side, "I'll be waiting for you," he reminded her.

Mekhay Doma finally reached her parents and gave the food provisions to them. They were happy to see her but soon they realized that she was very forlorn and cheerless and refused to eat any food at all. The mother was anxious and asked her, "Something is worrying you. Tell me. Maybe I can help you."

Mekhay Doma replied, "I am sad because this is the last time I shall be seeing you and father. There are three animals on the way home who are waiting to eat me."

The mother was a resourceful person and saying, "Don't you worry about that", she at once proceeded to make a huge barrel of *lac*. When the *lac* was heated and shaped into a *bumbu* or barrel she asked her daughter to get in. Then she closed the lid and rolled the barrel down the mountainside.

The leopard was waiting by the side of the road when the barrel rolled past him. "Whay, *bumbu*, have you seen Mekhay Doma?" questioned the leopard.

"*Ma thong , Ma thong. Nga ni bumbu runglungma, rung lung, rung lung song ma go*" (I haven't seen, I haven't seen. I am a round barrel and I must be on my way rulung, rulung)," replied the girl from the barrel.

Both the monkey and the pig were waiting when the barrel passed them. They asked for Mekhay Doma and she again said, "*Ma thong, ma thong. Nga ni bumbu runglungma, rung lung, rung lung songma go.*" As soon as she had said this the barrel hit a boulder and out came Mekhay Doma. The animals quickly seized her and prepared to cook her. The leopard went to collect the fire wood and the monkey went to fetch the water. The pig was to guard the girl.

Mekhay Doma sat against a big boulder and watched the pig as he browsed in the ground searching for roots and tubers and munching loudly, quite oblivious of his duty. She saw that he hardly looked in her direction. So she quickly dug a hole in the ground and hid in it.

After a while the leopard arrived with the firewood and the monkey with the water, "But where is the meat?" they both exclaimed together.

"Yaaa, she must have escaped," said the boar, looking around, startled.

"Then you will have to be the meat," declared the leopard and the monkey and they caught him and killed him.

Mekhay Doma listened to all the confusion and the noise. Then the ground began to get hotter and hotter for the fire had been built right above her. After a while it was becoming quite unbearable and she had to move a little. As she moved the stones on which the pot had been placed moved a little too. The two animals suddenly pricked up their ears in alarm. Mekhay Doma by now could no longer bear the heat and at the risk of being caught again came out of her hiding place. As she emerged, the pot containing all the pieces of meat fell over, spilling everything. The leopard and the monkey both sprang backwards in fright and ran away into the forest saying, "What evil thing is this?"

After Mekhay Doma came out of the ground she dusted herself and looked around. None of the animals was there any more. She wondered what had happened to frighten them off. She rekindled the fire which was dying down, as the water from the pot had spilled on it and roasted some meat which she found there. She ate all she could and carried the rest of the meat home.

So Acho Tsagye *cut off the ears too.*

Acho *Tsagye*

Dangbo thik naki wenda, Dingbo thik naki wenda, there were two brothers. Neither of them could remember their parents for they had both died when the two boys were very young. The older brother was rather simple minded but the younger brother was clever and hard working. They loved and cared for each other dearly. The younger brother called his older brother Acho *Tsagye* or Elder Brother Slow Wit in affection and he came to be known by that name in the village. He was everybody's *Acho Tsagye.* He was a strong young man who was often called upon by the villagers to do jobs where physical strength was required.

One day the younger brother went out to plow his fields and he told his brother to make lunch and bring it to the field at midday. "Acho, please make sure that the food is very clean."

Acho prepared some rice. To go with the rice he cooked some meat and chili, together with circular slices of radish. Then he packed the rice in a **bangchung** and placed the meat, chili, and radish on the rice. Carrying the *bangchung* in one hand and a container of **singchang** in the other, he made his way to the fields. On the way he happened to come across a large pile of cow dung right in the middle of the road. Acho very politely asked the cow dung to move away saying that his brother had asked him to bring his lunch clean. The cow dung of course could not move. Acho *Tsagye* warned it saying, "If you don't move I'll have to move you."

Still the cow dung would not budge. So the elder brother laid down the food near the dung and picked up a large stone and threw it on the dung with force. The dung being quite fresh splattered and now the open *bangchung* was full of cow dung. Acho *Tsagye* wondered what he should to do next. Then suddenly he had an idea. He went to the nearest stream and began to wash the rice grains one by one.

It was now long past midday and the younger brother was hungry and worried. He waited, but Acho *Tsagye* did not come. So he decided to go and see what the matter was. When he found his brother leaning over the banks of a stream washing the rice grains one by one he was baffled and asked: "Why are you doing that, Acho?"

Acho *Tsagye* explained what had happened. The younger brother shook his head sadly in disbelief and said, "*Aye wa*, Acho, listen carefully. I will now go home and eat something. You go to the field and watch the oxen. Don't let them move away."

Acho *Tsagye* made himself comfortable under the shade of a tree. Lying deep in the soft grass he watched the oxen which were grazing nearby. Then he noticed that they were swishing their tails constantly. He thought, "Ya, I better tell them to stop moving their tails. My brother told me not to let them move."

So he went to the oxen and he told them to stop moving their tails. But the oxen continued swishing their tails as oxen do to keep away the flies. Acho *Tsagye* thought he had to stop them. After long and deep consideration he decided that he would cut off the tails so that they would not be able to move. When he cut off the tails the oxen began to flip their ears as oxen do. So Acho *Tsagye* cut off the ears too. Now the oxen began to run away in pain so he cut off their limbs too. When the younger brother came back to the field he witnessed the most gruesome scene and he was horrified. Acho *Tsagye* explained proudly how he had stopped the oxen from moving.

The younger brother was helpless and in a moment of extreme frustration decided to leave his brother and run away. Secretly he began to prepare for his escape. He got a large *tseseb* and every day he filled it up with provisions. Just on the day he was to go Acho *Tsagye* found the *tseseb*. He thought, "It looks like my brother is preparing for a journey. I would like to go with him," so he removed all the provisions from the *tseseb* and got into it himself. The younger brother saw that Acho *Tsagye* was not around so he thought this to be a good opportunity. He put his *tseseb* on his back and ran away. The younger brother walked for a long time. Then he rested his basket on his T-stick and thought aloud, "Here I am, I wonder where my Acho *Tsagye* is." Acho *Tsagye* heard this and he whispered, "I am right behind you."

The younger brother walked across valleys and climbed mountains. Now he was very tired. So he took the *tseseb* from his back and started to prepare a fire and clear the area a little so that he could camp there for the night. When he opened the *tseseb* to take out some food he was shocked, for it was Acho *Tsagye* who struggled out of the *tseseb*. He crawled out of the basket with a big grin on his face and stretched out his limbs luxuriously for he had sat cramped in the basket for the whole day. Nothing of the provisions the younger brother had so carefully packed for many days was in it. He was utterly exasperated.

"Don't worry, we'll spend the night in that house. I am sure we will also get some food there" said Acho *Tsagye* as he pointed to a huge house which was not very far from where they were.

The house was very big and very rich but there was nobody inside. So the brothers decided to hide in the ground floor of the house where the domestic animals are usually housed and see who came to occupy the house. The room was huge. The brothers soon noticed that there were different-sized holes in the ceiling of the room and wondered what they were for. They had not been in their hiding place very long when there was a tremendous thumping of feet on the ground so that it shook, and scores of voices roared and rumbled. Then through each of the holes in the ceiling a huge black furry tail hung down. The *sinpos* had sat down to their evening meal. There were tails of every size. But the biggest tail hung in the middle of all the tails. Acho *Tsagye* had a great urge to pull on the tails so he said, " Can I pull on one of the tails."

The younger brother, who was trembling with fear and scarcely daring to breathe, whispered: "No, no, don't you realize what tails these are? They are the tails of the *sinpos*. If you touch the tail we will surely be eaten."

But Acho *Tsagye* kept on persisting until the younger brother agreed, saying, "If it makes you happy, just touch one very gently."

Acho *Tsagye* rolled up his sleeves, spat into his palms, rubbed them together and seizing the largest tail, he began to pull it with all his might. The *sinpo* jumped up, Acho *Tsagye* banged his head on the ceiling, "dang". Then Acho *Tsagye* pulled with all his strength and the *sinpo* landed on the floor with a "byaak." This dang, byaak, dang, byaak continued for a long time. The other sinpos were so shocked and frightened that they all ran off with a tremendous thumping of their feet and the excited rumbling and roaring of their voices. The *sinpo* and Acho *Tsagye* were of equal strength and neither would give in. Finally the skin from the *sinpo's* tail came off. The *sinpo* howled in pain and ran off.

Complete silence reigned. Only the sound of the crickets and the occasional screech of an owl could be heard. The brothers waited anxiously but nothing came. Finally they crept out of their hiding place and ventured forth very quietly on tiptoe, but there was no cause for fear as there was not a single *sinpo* in the house. The two of them sat down and had the sumptuous meal that the *sinpos* had laid out but had only started to eat.

The next day the brothers knew that the *sinpos* would come back. So as dusk fell they hid in the roof truss. Soon there was the thundering of voices and the thumping of the feet as the *sinpos* came back to reclaim their house. The two brothers could watch the *sinpos* unseen from the roof truss. They were all huge heinous-looking ape-like human beings with lethal-looking fangs. One had a fang that grew upwards so that it touched the ceiling while the other fang grew downwards till it scratched the ground. They all had long tails. The biggest *sinpo* who was the leader had a raw skinless tail which he carefully nursed every now and then. Soon they made a big fire, on top of which they put an enormous pan of oil. As the oil was being heated Acho *Tsagye* had the urgent need to relieve himself.

"I need to urinate. Can I urinate into the pan?" The younger brother who was trying to hold his rattling teeth begged him not to. Acho *Tsagye* kept on insisting. Finally the younger brother said, "If it will make you happy, but just one drop. Please only one drop." A huge smile of relief spread over his entire face as he began to relieve himself right into the hot pan of oil. The whole pan became a ball of fire and the sparks soon caught on to the fur of the *sinpos* and they began to shriek and holler in panic. They got up and started to run away, roaring and screeching with pain.

The two brothers got out of their hiding place and made a meal for themselves and slept peacefully that night. The *sinpos* did not come back and so the brothers took over the house. There was enough food and clothes to last them for many lifetimes and they were very happy.

One evening, many days after the *sinpos* had run away, they were eating *leab*, a thick soup prepared from buckwheat flour with tender buckwheat leaves and juicy bones flavored with pungent acorn peppers. Suddenly they heard the same roaring of voices and the thumping of feet and the *sinpos* came into the house, shouting, "We'll tear them apart. We'll eat their hot flesh and drink up their hot blood." At once the younger brother got up and began to wrestle with one of the *sinpos*. But Acho *Tsagye* continued eating his soup, warning them, "Ya, ya, be careful. You can wrestle as much as you like but don't spill my soup."

The younger brother was soon tired and worn out and he knew he was losing the fight. He had to think of something quickly to save himself. He saw his brother sitting in the middle of the room slurping up his soup quite oblivious of what was happening. So he began to edge towards where his brother was sitting. Finally when he could reach the soup bowl with his toes, he kicked it over. At this Acho *Tsagye* became uncontrollably violent and got up, saying, "Well, if you can't wrestle without spilling my soup I'll have to join in too." He then began systematically to pick up the *sinpos* one by one and swung them over his head like slings and threw them across the hills and over the mountains. The whole area was filled with the wailing of the defeated *sinpos*. The moans grew fainter and more distant and finally nothing could be heard. The *sinpos* would never come back now and the two brothers lived happily and comfortably for the rest of their lives.

He could feel all sorts of sensations and he was sure it was the fish.

The Silly Leopard

Dangbo..o..o Dingbo..o..o.. in a dense forest, somewhere in the rugged Bhutanese mountains, there was a leopard. He had been grievously humiliated by a fox who had played a nasty trick on him. He swore that he would catch the fox and kill him. He traveled all over the forest looking for the fox. One day he saw the fox sitting on the bank of a lake completely preoccupied with something. The leopard at once went towards him. As soon as the fox saw him coming, he gestured to him to be quiet. This made the leopard even more angry and he shouted, "You nasty fox, you think you can trick me again? This time I am going to kill you."

At this the fox pretended to be very surprised and said as calmly as possible, "Tell me, what is your problem? Maybe I can help you."

"That nasty trick that you played on me has made me the laughing stock of the entire forest."

"Which forest?" asked the fox.

"The forest behind the hill," replied the leopard.

"I knew it," said the fox, "there had to be a mistake. I never go beyond the shores of the lake. I belong to the clan of the peaceful fishing fox. We fish for our food and can only live where there is water and fish."

The leopard's curiosity was at once roused. "How do you fish?" he asked.

"It's quite simple. I just have to sit with my tail dipped in the lake and the fish hang onto it. Then I pull out my tail and there is always more fish than I can eat."

"Please let me try," said the leopard.

"Oh, no, this is our means of living, so I cannot let you do it."

"Please, please, just once," begged the foolish leopard.

"All right, just this once. Now you must sit very still with your tail dipped in the water and you must pull it out only when the first rays of the morning sun touch the tops of the trees." So saying the fox sprinted off and disappeared into the forest.

It was winter time, and the lake froze in the night. Sitting in the bright moonlight night watching the sparkling stars, the leopard thrilled at the idea of all the fish attaching themselves to his tail. He could feel all sorts of sensations and he was sure it was the fish. As the first rays of the sun touched the tops of the trees in the forest he tried to pull out his tail but it was frozen fast and he had to struggle and pull vigorously for a long time. Finally he could free himself but the skin from his tail remained frozen in the lake. He howled in pain. Now he was even more determined to catch up with the fox and kill him.

After several days of searching, he spied the fox sitting crouched on his hind legs, holding a drum stick between his paws and chanting strange words and hitting the ground with the drum stick. The leopard jumped upon him and seized him, shouting, "You trickster, look what you have done to me. I am going to kill you!"

Feigning complete innocence the fox said, "I do not know what you are talking about. Before you kill me at least tell me what happened."

The leopard explained in great detail how the fox had tricked him the first time and made him the laughing stock of the entire forest and how the fox had again tricked him and made him lose the skin off his tail. On hearing this the fox clicked his tongue and shook his head in sympathy and said, "I wish I had met you before, I could have warned you. Those foxes living on the banks of that lake happen to be my distant cousins and they are known for their trickery. I am so ashamed of them. Please allow me to tell you how sorry I am for your misfortunes."

The silly leopard at once believed the fox and asked him what he was doing. Of course, the fox was just waiting for the leopard to ask him that question. The fox laid down his drum sticks and looking at them fondly, he said, "I am a drum fox. I live by drumming. I hit the ground and when I have drummed it enough and chanted all the right words, delicious honey just pours out of the ground. I do not eat anything but honey so I do not go anywhere beyond this area."

Once again the leopard became very curious and asked, "Do you think I could try some of the honey?"

"Of course you can try, but at the moment I don't have any. In fact if you had not stopped to talk with me, I was just ready to get some."

"Please let me try. What should I do?"

The cunning fox looked around, saying, "As you will be tasting the honey only once in your lifetime let me find the best spot for you."

Having said this he put his ear to the ground and listened to the steady buzz of bees in an underground hive. Then he taught the leopard some nonsensical words and asked him to hit on the ground with the drum sticks as hard as he could. The leopard took the drum sticks and chanting the nonsensical words he began to hit the ground with great enthusiasm. By this time the cunning fox had quietly walked off without even so much as a backward glance.

It was not long before the ground broke open and the angry swarm of frenzied bees came bursting out, with great ferocity and stung the leopard mercilessly. He shrieked and waved his paws and jumped on his hind legs but the thoroughly infuriated bees would not leave him till they were satisfied.

The leopard was very sore and covered with lumps and bumps. Now he was very bitter and he swore that he would not let the fox get away this time. He wandered around the forest for days until he caught up with the fox once again. The fox was sitting in a *yuva*, a large storage container woven out of bamboo, on the edge of a cliff and rocking gently and singing to himself. The leopard jumped upon him with his most classic roar and said, "If I don't kill you who will I kill? You wicked fox, you tricked me three times. Now there is no way of letting you go."

But the fox replied, "I think you and I have suffered the same fate. I too have been so badly mistreated by my family and relatives that I have come to live by myself away from them all and I am quite content to look at the whole world from this basket. This basket is wonderful. From it, I can not only see the whole world but I feel neither hunger nor thirst."

The leopard had not learnt his lesson and on hearing this his resolve to kill the fox vanished and he begged to go into the basket. The fox agreed after much pleading on the part of the leopard.

"You must stay only for a very short time, please," said the fox as he reluctantly got out of the basket. The leopard was so eager that he jumped in. No sooner had he jumped in than the fox pushed the basket over the cliff and that was the end of the silly leopard.

Gyalpo Migkarla

Dangbo..o..o Dingbo..o..o.. in a small house nearly falling apart with age and neglect there lived an old couple. The old man would sit by the hearth rubbing his swollen right knee and moaning and groaning in pain. The old woman did all the work in the house. One day she was rather tired and not in a very agreeable mood. While she cooked at the stove she asked the old man to pass her the ladle which was hanging near him but the old man would not even do that. As usual he just sat there rubbing his knee and moaning away. Irritated by his behavior, she said sharply, "Move this knee away, it's in my way."

But the old man did not pay any attention to her request. So she took up a ladle and struck the knee with all her strength. They were both equally shocked when the swollen knee burst with a great splosh and a big ugly frog popped out. The old woman caught it by its hind legs before it could hop away and, dangling it in the air, she said, "So you were the cause of all my old man's problems! Now, if I don't kill you who will I kill?" She was ready to throw him into the fire when the frog croaked miserably, "Please, I beg of you, don't kill me, I'll be useful to you."

The old woman laughed and asked, "What, a frog be useful? I have never heard of such a thing. How can a frog be useful?"

"I'll bring home a bride," promised the frog.

"Ya, ya, if you can bring home a bride I'll spare you," agreed the old woman.

The frog immediately went to the king's palace. He hid under a big slab of stone and shouted, "Oh, king, I want one of your daughters as my bride!" The king asked his oldest daughter Langyamo to go and see who was shouting. She looked out and reported, "The chickens are

So the next day the king disguised himself as Jow Pha La Phan Chung and went to plow the field.

scratching in the dirt, the pigs are browsing around and there is nobody else."

Again the frog called. This time the king sent his second daughter, Khempamo, to see if there was anybody outside. She too went out and came back, saying, "The chickens are scratching in the dirt and the pigs are browsing around other than them there is nobody."

The frog called for the third time and this time the king asked his third daughter Phurzamo, to go out and see who had called. When she looked around, she saw a big ugly frog sitting on a slab of stone. She came in and said, "There is a frog on the stone slab."

The king said, "Call the frog in, perhaps he has something to tell us."

The frog hopped into the palace and stood in front of the king reverently but boldly stated, "I would like to take one of your daughters as my wife." The king was greatly insulted and angrily said, "You lowly, impudent, ugly frog, what makes you think that one of my daughters will agree to marry you?"

The frog warned, "If you don't give me a bride I'll cry."

"Go ahead and cry. I am not afraid of a crying frog," said the king.

The frog began to cry. His tears flowed like two great rivers and the king's palace shuddered and shook as if it was going to be washed away.

"Please stop. You may have a bride." The frog stopped crying and everything became normal.

"Now who will come as my bride?" asked the frog.

"None of us," replied the girls haughtily.

At this the frog began to laugh in a deep throaty croak-like laugh. As he laughed the entire palace began to tremble and shake. The walls began to crack and the beams caved in. "Please stop at once and take the bride of your choice," pleaded the king.

The king turned to his oldest daughter and asked her to go as the frog's bride but she refused condescending, stating, "Rather than marry a frog I'll go to the bear," and she went and married a bear.

The second daughter said, "I'll marry a leopard instead of the frog," and she too went off.

The third girl had no choice but to agree to become the frog's bride. The frog led his bride home. The two old people, who were so feeble with age and weak with hunger that they could not take the shock of seeing the frog with a princess, both swooned and died of bewilderment.

Now the frog and Phurzamo lived together for many days. One day Phurzamo saw that her frog husband was not really a frog. As she secretly watched him he took off the skin and out came a very handsome young man. She at once ran to him and picked up his frog skin but he cautioned her, "Don't destroy it! It is useful." He then instructed her on what she should do with his frog skin. According to his instructions she shook the skin in all the rooms of the house, around the house and across the valleys and on the sides of the hills.

"Now burn it," he cried. And so she did.

The next morning when Phurzamo woke up she was pleasantly surprised to see herself in a beautiful palace with everything that she could dream of. There were jewelry and clothes in her rooms. The granaries were full. Servants stood around waiting to do as she would bid them. The valleys were full of crops and cattle and horses grazed on the hillsides. She could not have asked for more. They lived happily together for many days.

Soon Phurzamo's sister Khempamo heard what had happened and she became very jealous. So she visited her sister with the intention of killing her and marrying her husband. She carried her leopard babies on her back wrapped in moss and tied with creepers. She invited her sister to go for a walk and to bathe in the stream. They walked away from the house and as soon they reached a stream, Phurzamo said, "Let's bathe here."

But the sister said," *A kha khai*, don't you know this is an *acchu*? Let's go a little further." So they walked on until they reached another stream.

Again Phurzamo said, "This looks like a clean stream, let's bathe here."

But again the sister said, "*A kha khai*, don't you know that there is the cremation ground just up the stream?" So they walked on until they eventually reached a lake. The sister pointed to the lake and said, "This is where we will bathe." So the girls took off their necklaces, unhooked their *komas*, and let their *kiras*, fall off their shoulders and hang down from their waists. They were bare up to their waists and they began to wash themselves by the side of the lake. Then Khempamo said, "Here, let me rub your back for you," and began to do so. After a while she tried to push her sister into the lake. Phurzamo was startled and asked, "What are you trying to do, are you trying to push me into the lake?"

At this Khempamo apologized, saying "No, no, of course not. It's this little finger of mine," and she ate it up, for she was a demon. After a while she gave one big push and Phurzamo drowned in the lake.

Khempamo then put on the necklace and the *komas* of her drowned sister and returned to the palace, pretending to be her sister. Although the king did not see a difference the child at once saw that this was not her mother and began to cry and fuss. Many days passed and the king began to realize that there was something different about his wife but he was still not sure. Before long it was too late and he was completely under her control.

Now it happened that the king owned some fields near the lake. One day one of his servants called Jow Pha La Phan Chung was plowing around the lake when suddenly a tall bamboo grew out of the lake. A bird sat on the top of it and began to sing. It sang, "Jow Pha La Phan Chung, Jow Pha La Phan Chung, how is my child, what does the demoness feed my child? What does she serve *Gyalpo Migkarla* and what does she give you?"

Jow Pha La Phan Chung at once recognized the bird to be Phurzamo and replied, "The demoness feeds your child ash, the king *karmatekpa* and me rice water."

On hearing this the bird quickly disappeared into the water.

When Jow Pha La Phan Chung returned home in the evening he told the king about his encounter with the bird. So the next day the king went to plow the field near the lake, but the bird did not come out. Disillusioned the king told Jow Pha La Phan Chung that the bird had not come out of the lake. "She probably recognized you. You had better disguise yourself tomorrow," he suggested.

So the next day the king disguised himself as Jow Pha La Phan Chung and went to plow the field. After a while a tall bamboo grew out of the lake and a small bird sat on it. Again the bird sang the song asking after her child and *Gyalpo Migkarla*. The king spoke to the bird and said, "If you are indeed my wife fly onto the back of my ox." The bird flew onto the hump of the ox. Then the king again said, "If you are truly my wife fly onto the horn of the ox." The bird flew onto the horn. The king then picked up the bird and took it home. He put the bird in a golden cage and looked after it lovingly.

One day the king had to go on a journey and when he returned he realized that the demoness, Khempamo, had eaten the bird. "Please tell me, is there nothing left of my bird?" pleaded the king.

"There may be some bones in the refuse behind the door," replied Khempamo. So the king patiently sorted out every bit of the refuse behind the door until he found a tiny bird bone. The bone spoke saying, "*Sang tang, sur tang, dhar dang gochen nang la pud.*(Burn incense and other offerings to the spirits and wrap it in brocades and silk)." So the king washed it, burnt incense, wrapped it in silk and brocade and put it in a small container. Every day he repeated the same procedure, each time increasing the size of the container and each time the bone would grow bigger and fill the container so that eventually he placed the bone in a clean room, burnt incense, and covered it with silks and brocade. When he went into the room the next morning he was filled with immeasurable happiness when he saw wife standing there more beautiful then ever.

The royal couple beseeched their *tsawa lama* to come to their palace and perform the rites of subjugation to subdue the demoness Khempamo. The demoness was thus vanquished and the king and the queen could now once again live in peace, prosperity and happiness.

(We often refer to a person as being *mikarla* or white eyed if they do not see the obvious flaws in a person.)

Bum Sing Sing Yangdonma

Dangbo..o..o Dingbo..o..o.. in a small village in the middle of a narrow valley surrounded by mountains, somewhere in Bhutan, there lived a young girl. Her mother had died a long time ago so she lived alone with her father. The father worked on the narrow strips of land along the river banks where he grew wheat and barley. The girl wove beautiful fabrics at her backstrap loom which was hung on the little porch outside their house. Every day she sat at her loom working intricate designs into the fabrics that she wove.

One day she was sitting at her loom weaving when a raven flew by and dropped a piece of a fruit in front of her. She picked it up and looked at it. She had never seen a fruit like this before but it smelled so sweet and looked so temptingly good that she ate it and it was the most delicious fruit she had ever eaten and she longed for more. At sunset her father came home from the fields and she excitedly told him about the bird and the fruit and asked him to get her some more. The father said, "My daughter, this is not an ordinary fruit. It is a mandarin which grows only in the *sinpo's* orchard." But the daughter pleaded and begged as one bewitched, "*Apa*, please, I must have more of this fruit or I shall never be happy."

The orchard was in the next valley although the *sinpo* himself lived in the distant *sinpoiyul*. Nobody even dared to go near the orchard. The poor father, unable to deny anything to his only daughter, reluctantly but eventually agreed to go and steal some fruit from the *sinpo's* orchard. In the darkness of the night the father headed towards the *sinpo's* orchard stealthily, creeping on tiptoe. When he reached the orchard he saw that the *sinpo* was sitting, and

"What can you do for me?" asked the sinpo, not relenting in one way or the other.

leaning against the tree, and was fast asleep. He was snoring fiercely. The father crept up to the tree. The *sinpo* continued to sleep on and the brave man climbed up the tree very quietly. The *sinpo* still slept on. Now the father was among the branches plucking the ripe fruits and filling up his bag. Soon the bag was full and it grew heavy. But he wanted more so he continued, plucking more and more when, suddenly, the strap of the bag broke and the mandarins fell down, with the bag and all. One mandarin struck the *sinpo* on the head and he woke up with a start. The father shivered as he climbed down the tree and faced the ferocious sinpo.

The *sinpo* was furious and roared, "I am going to kill you. You not only stole my mandarins but also had the audacity to throw one at me."

"I beg for your mercy. I have done you wrong. I will do anything for you if you will spare me my life," pleaded the father.

"What can you do for me?" asked the *sinpo*, not relenting in one way or the other.

At this, the father said, "Anything. Anything at all."

So the *sinpo* said, "If that is true, then I want your daughter to come as my bride."

This was a terrible shock to the father of a single daughter, one who was loved so dearly, but he could not refuse this proposition as he had agreed to do anything. As a last resort he added a condition. "I will send her to you if you can find out her name." The *sinpo* agreed.

The *sinpo* asked a pig to go and find out the girl's name. Quietly the pig hid in the bushes and waited for someone to call the girl by her name. Before the end of the day he heard the father call his daughter and the pig learnt the name. He rushed home, all the time repeating the name, "Sing Sing Yangdonma, Sing Sing Yangdonma," for that was the name of the girl. Just before he reached the *sinpo's* house he saw some thick juicy roots by the wayside and he decided to have a quick browse. He enjoyed the roots so much that he stayed on until he had had his fill and he had forgotten the name.

When he stood in front of the *sinpo* all he could do was grunt, "Yoush Yoush," as all pigs do. The *sinpo* was angry and had him for his dinner.

On the second day the *sinpo* sent a monkey to find out the girl's name. The monkey hid in the branches of a tree near the girl's house until he too found out the name. He rushed home swinging from tree to tree and repeating the name until he came across some ripe golden bananas. He stopped to eat the bananas and forgot the name. When the *sinpo* demanded to know the name all the monkey could do was bare all his teeth and chatter, for although he scratched his head sore he could not remember the name. Annoyed by the monkey's failure the *sinpo* ate him too.

On the third day the *sinpo* sent a honey bee. She sat patiently on the window sill all day until she found out the name of the girl and then she flew to the *sinpo*. She buzzed along, all the way repeating the name, "Sing Sing Yangdonma, Sing Sing Yangdonma, Sing Sing…." The *sinpo* was pleased and the bee was not eaten. Even to this day the honey bee still says, "sing sing sing".

The *sinpo* at once went to the house of Sing Sing Yangdonma and took her away with him. They had to travel for many days past many mountains and valleys. One day they passed a magnificent valley with beautiful hues. The sky was ablaze with the richest colors. The mountains and the valley had tinges of all the colors. Even the trees, plants, and animals were colorful and bright. Sing Sing Yangdonma asked, "Is this where you live?"

"No, somebody else lives here. *Za* lives here."

Then they reached a huge rocky mountain where everything looked red. There was a big red *dzong* among the rocks. Sing Sing Yangdonma asked again, "Is this your house?"

"No, it's somebody else's." It belongs to *Tsen*."

Finally they reached a huge valley that was barren and bare. Everything had an ashy-gray appearance. In the middle of this emptiness stood a huge monstrous house. The house was built up of bones of every kind. The pillars were made of human thigh bones and the roof was covered with human skins. Sing Sing Yangdonma was horrified and filled with intense depression. There was not a dog nor a human to be seen or heard. An eerie silence filled the atmosphere. She knew that this was the house of the *sinpo*.

On reaching the house the *sinpo* at once tied Sing Sing Yangdonma in a big basket and hung her upside down from the ceiling. He told his daughter to keep watch on her. Sing Sing Yangdonma sank into deep despair for she knew that she could never escape from the *sinpo* and she began to cry as if her heart would break. All of a sudden she had an idea. She began to sing from the basket, "I am so happy in this basket, I can see India and I can see Tibet. I never want to get out of this basket."

The words of the song soon caught the *sinpo's* daughter's attention and she became very curious. She listened to the song carefully and it was the same again and again. Finally she asked Sing Sing Yangdonma, "Can you really see India and Tibet from the basket?"

"Of course, that's why I would never want to get out of the basket," replied Sing Sing Yangdonma with feigned cheerfulness.

"Can I see India and Tibet for a while?"

Sing Sing Yangdonma would not agree but the *sinpo's* daughter was very persuasive. "Please let me see India and Tibet just for a while."

Finally she agreed, saying, "Very well but mind you, just for a while."

The *sinpo's* daughter quickly helped Sing Sing Yangdonma out of the basket and got into it herself. Sing Sing Yangdonma tied her up securely and immersed the basket into a big pot of boiling water. After the *sinpo's* daughter was scalded to death Sing Sing Yangdonma took the bunch of keys which was hanging from a hook on the wall and began to open all the locked doors in the house. In one room there were many young children. In the second room there were hundreds of young adults. In the third room there were middle-aged women and in the fourth room middle-aged men. She released them all. In the last room there was a lone old woman. As the light entered the dark room the old woman shielded her eyes for she had not seen light for many years. Then she blinked her ancient eyes and stared at the girl in front of her in total disbelief. Finally she whispered, "How did you find me? Please run away before the *sinpo* comes. He will eat both of us. I was brought here as his bride when I was a young girl. You see, now that I am old he has thrown me into this room and forgotten about me. But one day when he has nothing better to eat he will eat me too. Here, take my skin," said the old woman as she slipped off her skin and pulled it over her head. Then she added, "Take all the jewels you can carry from the next room. Then run away as fast as you can." Sing Sing Yangdonma took strings and strings of coral and turquoise and put on earrings and bracelets and then she slipped the old woman's skin over herself and ran away as fast as her feet could carry her.

The *sinpo* soon found out what had happened and he began to chase Sing Sing Yangdonma. She could never have run away from him because he crossed mountains in a few steps and he could straddle a valley with his legs planted on either side of the river, so when she reached a valley with some houses she recognized to be human houses she decided to try and trick the *sinpo*. She sat down by the road side and turned her back to the sun as old people often do to get the sun on their backs. As she sat thus she chanted, "**Om Mani Padme Hung**." The *sinpo* soon caught up with her and he asked impatiently, "Have you seen Sing Sing Yangdonma pass this way?"

"No, I haven't seen anyone pass this way, I have been sitting here for a long time now," lied Sing Sing Yangdonma.

"Then get out of my way, you old woman!" grunted the *sinpo* as he pushed her aside. The jewelry made the sound "tsalak tsalak" and the *sinpo* looked at her suspiciously and asked, "What was that?"

"U ...hoo u ...hoo, those were my old bones creaking and crack-ing, krack krock," replied Sing Sing Yangdonma matter-of-factly and pretended to rub her elbows and knees in earnest.

Sing Sing Yangdonma sat in the sun, immensely relieved that the *sinpo* had not recognized her. By and by three young men came along the road. They were the sons of the king of the valley. They had gone to cut bamboo and were now pulling it home. Each man had forty long bamboo poles tied in a bundle and strapped to his back and as they walked the tips of the bamboo touched the ground, making a continuous sweeping sound "shor .. shor". As the first prince came by he shouted, "Old Woman, get out of my way!"

Sing Sing Yangdonma refused to move out of the way, saying, "If you are in a hurry step over me and if you are not in a hurry go around me."

The first prince went right over her and the second prince did the same. The third prince felt sorry for the old woman and went off the road so that he would not go over her. As he passed by the tips of his bamboo touched her and she fell over. The jewelry made the "tsalak tsalak" sound. The third prince was so anxious that he had hurt her and he at once put his bamboo down and came to help her. As Sing Sing Yangdonma watched him go, after he had helped her, she thought: "He is surely the kindest of them all."

Many days later Sing Sing Yangdonma was sure that the sinpo would not come after her any more. So she went to a nearby steam to bathe herself. She slipped off the old woman's skin and washed herself in the stream. The youngest prince who happened to be near the stream saw this. He was amazed to see that the old woman was no longer an old woman but a beautiful young girl. *She was so beautiful that she would have melted in the sunshine and solidified in the shade.* He immediately fell in love with her and married her. They lived for many years together in happiness, peace, and prosperity.

The boy crept quietly all over the cave and was astounded at all the precious jewels and exquisite thro zangs *that lay all over the place.*

Ap Braphu

Dangbo..o..o Dingbo..o..oo.. there was a poor boy. All he had was a cow, so every day he went with the cow to the forest and let her graze there. As the animal grazed in the grassy patches under the trees he would collect firewood. One day he carelessly wandered too far from the forest clearing where the cow was grazing and when he returned to look for her she was nowhere in sight. Anxiously he searched the forest, calling the animal by her name, "Zaykarmo, Zaykarmo". But there was no sign of the cow. She was truly lost.

The sun was already setting and darkness was fast descending so he decided to resume the search the next day. He heaved the huge load of firewood upon his back and began to retrace his steps home. Suddenly he stopped, for there, just a few paces in front of him, was the most unusual sight. Near a massive rock sat an old lady who was trembling and shivering with intense cold. She was so old that she was all shriveled up and full of wrinkles. She was blind and she had an enormous goiter. The boy hid in the bushes and watched her for he had never seen anyone like her before. After the sun had set completely the old woman whose teeth were now rattling (for one her age she had strong white teeth) put her hands on the ground to support herself and rose up very slowly. Saying *"ah chu chu chu,"* she turned towards the rock and said, *"Ap Braphu, Go Phich* (Father Cave, open the door)." Suddenly a portion of the rock moved and opened up, with a big sound drrrrr..b and the old woman hobbled inside. The boy waited for a while and then went in front of the rock and said *"Ap Braphu, Go Phich,"* nervously as he cast quick glances in all directions, like a fugitive being pursued, for he felt uneasy as if he was being watched. The door to the cave opened up and he too went inside. Once inside the cave he was amazed to see that it was a very comfortable home. As he wandered around the house he saw the woman. She seemed to be perpetually cold and she had already made a fire in the hearth. There she was sitting in front of the crackling fire, warming herself.

The boy crept quietly all over the cave and was astounded at all the precious jewels and exquisite *thro zangs* that lay all over the place. He collected as many as he could possibly carry and waited for morning. The next morning the boy watched what the old woman would do. At about sunrise the old woman went to the cave door and said *"Ap Braphu, Go Phich"* and the cave door opened. The old woman went out of the rock and sat there in front of it sunning herself. The poor boy quickly got out of the rock and hurried back to the village. He told his friends about his adventure in the forest. The rich boy, on hearing this and seeing all the jewels and treasures, thought, "I have to get some of those things too," and promptly headed towards the forest. Everything was true. There was the old woman and the rock which opened up, and the treasures too. While the rich boy was in the cave the old woman sensed the presence of a human being and she began to grope and feel around in the cave muttering, *"Ane, ane,* let me eat the fresh meat and let me drink the hot blood." Soon she found him and before the boy could get out of the cave she caught and killed and devoured him. This old woman was a demoness of the rocks who waited for unfortunate victims to come wandering to her for she was so old that she was no longer able to hunt for her prey.

The Tale Of The Goat's Tail

Dangbo..o..o thik naki wenda Dingbo..o..o thik naki wenda… there was an old man and an old woman. They did not have any children and as they were old and could not work any longer, they did not have much to eat. They had eaten everything they had in their possession and now all they had was a fairly large goat.

One day the old man had an idea and said, "We have this goat but it is of no use to us while it lives. It would be best to eat it."

At this the old woman asked, "How shall we kill the goat? We have never killed a goat before."

The old man told her that he had a very good plan and so he explained, "We will pull the goat apart. You hold him by the tail and I will hold onto the horns and we will pull with all our strength and keep for ourselves whatever we get." The old woman thought that this was a good idea and enthusiastically agreed.

So the old man held the goat by the horns and the old woman held onto its tail and at the count of three they pulled and pulled and pulled. Suddenly they fell on their backs with the portion of the goat they had each managed to pull. The old man had the whole goat except for the tail and all that the old woman had was the tail!

Every day the old woman sat swallowing her spit as she watched the old man eat the goat meat in different ways. He had fried meat, minced meat, roasted meat, and stewed meat. One day the old man gave her some bones. She decided to make a soup with the bones so she began to chop them up. Every time she chopped the bone the goat's tail mimicked the noise. So as her knife made the tok tok sound against the chopping board the goat's tail also cried "tok tok" from the shelf on which it was kept. This annoyed the woman

The old man had the whole goat except for the tail and all that the old woman had was the tail!

and she warned, "If you do not stop imitating me, I'll roast you in the ashes and eat you too." But the goat's tail continued to mimic her. She was so enraged that she finally got up in a huff and took the tail to the fire. At this the goat's tail began to plead, saying, "Please spare me my life and I will repay you." Surprised the woman asked how a tail could possibly do anything. But the goat's tail begged her and she agreed that she would spare him for three days, during which time he would have to prove himself.

The goat's tail went to a flour mill where a girl had just finished milling her wheat. She gathered and scraped all the flour from the mill stone and filled her leather bag. Then she sat down and tried to carry the bag but she could not even make it budge because the goat's tail was hiding under the bag and pulling it back with all the energy he possessed. The girl was quite surprised because she usually had no problem carrying home such a bag. She then took out some flour and put it into another bag and tried again without any success. This time she took off her *toigo* or jacket, and tied knots at the ends of the sleeves and filled them up with more flour from the bag. Even then she could not carry the bag. Quite distressed the girl went home to call somebody to help her to carry home the bag. As soon as the girl went the goat's tail picked up the bag and ran home with it. The old woman was delighted and agreed to let him live for a few more days.

The next day the goat's tail went into the king's pastures and selected a big bull. He killed it and took it home to the old woman who was now very happy with her goat's tail. The goat's tail took the tail of the bull and stuck half of it into the marsh to make is appear as if the whole bull had sunk into the marsh with only a bit of the tail sticking out. Then he rushed to the king's palace and reported that the king's servants had allowed his best bull to sink into the marsh. The king sent all his servants to pull out the bull. While the men tried to pull the tail out of the marsh the goat's tail pushed it deeper into the marsh and eventually the whole tail disappeared into the marsh. The king had lost his best bull!

Now the king wanted to test his servants to see if they were really as irresponsible as the goat's tail had accused them of being. It happened that the king had a *norbu*, a very precious wish-fulfilling jewel in his treasury, and he was so confident of the security of his palace that he challenged, "Anybody who can steal the jewel will get not only half my kingdom but also my daughter as his bride."

The goat's tail decided to try to steal the jewel, so he made elaborate plans. He got several leather bags, some boulders, and prepared *tsendili*, a slippery substance made of the cooked roots of a plant that grows wild. When he was ready he announced that he would come to steal the jewel. The king naturally made sure that everything was done to foil the theft. Everybody was on the alert as they waited for the thief. The goat's tail waited and waited until everybody else was so tired of waiting that they had became sleepy. Then he slipped into the stable. All the horses were saddled and ready. He led the horses to the sheep shed and guided the sheep into the stables. He fed the guard dogs with juicy pieces of meat so that they did not attack him, and then he made them change their places with the cattle. After this he poured water onto the bundles of wood splinters that had been prepared for torches. As he climbed the wooden stairs he smeared each step with *tsendili*. He next went to the royal attendants who were sitting in wait but were now dozing off. The goat's tail quietly tied stones to the ends of the *kabne* or ceremonial shawls of these men and covered their heads with the leather bags. When he was absolutely sure that everything had been taken care of he slipped through the chink in the wall, seized the jewel, and left the same way. As he walked through the court-yard he shouted at the top of his voice, "O king, the thief has stolen the *norbu*." Then what followed was utter confusion and chaos as the attendants tried to get the leather bags off their heads, all the time muttering, "These leather bags, these leather bags." Finally, when they managed to pull the leather bags off their heads they flung their *kabne* over their shoulders trying to put them in place properly. But as they flung their *kabne* the boulders tied to the ends of them struck each other and there were terrible moans and groans in the dark. They ran down the steps but they slipped, as the stairs were smeared with slippery *tsendili* and there was a pile of men at the bottom of the stairs. The torches were wet and it was impossible to light them. So in total darkness, "Release the dogs!" ordered the king, but instead of the ferocious barks the mooing of the cattle could be heard. "Onto the horses and after the thief!" But instead of the ready-saddled horses the bleating sheep scattered in all directions adding to the commotion. By this time the goat's tail was in the safety of the old woman's house, proudly showing the *norbu* to the old woman ...

The next day the goat's tail went to claim his reward. The king could not refuse so the goat's tail took half the kingdom and the princess. When he reached home he called to the old woman to open the door. But the old woman simply responded saying, "Come by your usual way through the hole in the latch."

The goat's tail said, "Even if the horse would fit the saddle would not fit and even if the saddle would fit the bride would not fit." At this the old woman rushed to open the door.

Once a year all the people of the village stopped working, put on their best clothes, and went to the village festival. It was the most important event for the village. The goat's tail insisted that the princess should go to the festival and that he would stay home to look after the house. In the evening when the princess came home the goat's tail asked her who in her opinion was the most beautiful girl at the festival and who was the handsomest man. At this the princess coyly replied saying that she, herself was the most beautiful girl but she could not tell the name of the handsomest man because he did not stop to talk with anybody. He just sat astride his beautifully decked horse and rode through the crowd while the crowd looked at him in admiration and awe and wondered, "Who can this man be?"

The next day the princess again went to the festival and when she came home in the evening the goat's tail again asked her the same question. She gave the same answer as on the previous day. The next morning when the goat's tail asked her to go to the festival again, she became very suspicious so she pretended to go but actually hid near the house and watched what the goat's tail was up to. At about midday the goat's tail shed its skin and out came the handsome man she had seen on the two previous days. Without a word she jumped out from her hiding place and took up the skin of the goat's tail. Before her husband could stop her, she threw it into the fire, saying that she would no longer be humiliated as the wife of a goat's tail. The goat's tail was completely devastated and he sadly explained, "Tonight I would have been free of my destiny as a goat's tail and I would have told you everything. If you had only waited a little longer." He then told her to collect all the ashes and sprinkle them in all the rooms of the house, then in the yard and finally in the meadows and on the hillsides. When she sprinkled the ashes in the rooms they filled up with wealth, and servants rushed around ready to take their orders. Horses and hens and roosters appeared as she sprinkled the ashes in the yard. The meadows filled up with cattle as she sprinkled the ashes there. Herds of yaks appeared on the hillsides as she sprinkled the last specks of ash. As the time had not been right everything had some small defect, so the clothes had torn seams or a missing collar. The utensils had slight dents, the animals had missing tails and ears and some of the roosters even had no combs! The man looked at his new possessions and thoughtfully stated, "We can never escape our destiny."

The Ghost with the Water Goiter

Dangbo..o..o Dingbo..o..o.. there was a solitary house on a hill, surrounded by ruins. Many, many years ago an entire village had been devastated by an epidemic and most of the inhabitants had either died or moved away. The vacant houses soon succumbed to the ravages of age and weather and now all that was left were bleak and crumbling ruins. Paydon and her brother lived in that solitary and desolate house. One day the brother had to go on a journey for a few days so he said, "I will not be home for some days. Don't forget to feed the rooster well and he will be a good companion to you." The girl fed the rooster every day but one day she forgot to feed it. That evening when it became dark the rooster dipped its wings in water and sprinkled water on the fire and put it out. So Paydon had to go and search for fire.

Paydon walked through the forest for a long time and eventually she saw smoke rising at the far end of the forest. She followed the smoke and at last reached a shed where an old woman with an enormous goiter was sitting beside a flickering fire, spinning wool. Paydon approached the old woman and asked her for some fire. The old woman immediately withdrew a piece of burning wood from the fire and gave it to her. But as Paydon turned to go the old woman slipped a roll of yak-hair yarn into the fold of the sheep skin that Paydon was wearing on her back. The old woman held onto the end of the woolen yarn. Unaware, Paydon walked home and the yarn began to unravel. The old woman waited for a while and then followed the yarn. As she walked on she rolled the yarn into a ball. At the end of the yarn was Paydon's house.

Then he began to hit her with the iron hammer and pinch her with the iron clamps.

The old woman reached the house soon after Paydon had prepared her night meal. Pleased with the unusual company Paydon gladly shared her food with the visitor. After the meal she took out some wool and began to card and clean it. But very soon she noticed something very curious about the old woman. The size of the goiter seemed to alter with the intensity of the fire. Every time the fire blazed the goiter grew smaller, and as soon as the fire diminished and flickered the goiter began to swell. Paydon shivered in fear for she had heard of the ghost with the water goiter. Paydon knew that she must not sleep. She would have to feed the fire continuously to save herself. If the fire were to dwindle, the woman's goiter would swell and burst, splashing out water and in the darkness she would devour her victim. Paydon brought out a big basket of wool and worked on it to keep herself awake. She began to heap up logs of wood on the fire and kept it burning furiously. Soon her stock of wood was exhausted and as the last log burned slowly and shadows played on the walls, the goiter grew bigger and bigger. Poor Paydon thought hopelessly, "It's going to burst any moment now," when they were both startled with the sudden call of the rooster, "Cockerico, cockerico, cockerico," and the old woman left, for she knew that dawn was breaking.

The next day Paydon carried in all the firewood she had and she was well prepared to meet her adversary. She made the evening meal and before she could eat it the old woman was in front of her. She unflinchingly shared her meal with the woman and then she took out a huge container of dried beans and began to shell them. She fed the fire lavishly, so that it crackled and rose high above the stove. The old woman's goiter never grew bigger than an egg. She sat to the side of the stove irate and resentful watching Paydon with big eyes. When the rooster called she got up abruptly and shuffled out of the house without a word.

Thoroughly distressed, Paydon wondered how she could get enough firewood for the night. At the most she could carry home one load from the forest far away. She anxiously looked at the sun and the shadows for indications of time and as the sun touched the western mountain ranges all she could do was call upon her deities and collect the old bamboo fences around her house. She knew that these would burn brightly for a short while and quickly be reduced to ashes. So when her brother walked into the house a day earlier than he was expected back, she was sure it was her deities who had heeded her calls. She quickly told him all about the ghost with the goiter.

The brother calmly set about preparing to meet the visitor. He found two hammers, one of wood and the other of iron. He sorted out an old leather bag and a new leather bag from among the bags in the house. Finally he found a pair of wooden clamps and a pair of iron clamps. As darkness fell the old woman came into the house resolutely for she had made up her mind to eat Paydon at any cost. On seeing the brother in the house she angrily stormed, "Who has dared to eat before me?"

"I have," replied the brother.

"Who wishes to challenge me?"

"I dare to challenge you," quipped the brother.

"How shall we test our powers?" asked the old woman, her voice trembling with passion.

So the brother gave the wooden hammer, the wooden clamps, and the old leather bag to the old woman. But he kept for himself the iron hammer, the iron clamps, and the new leather bag. Then he got into the old bag. "Now you can tie me up in the leather bag. While I am in the bag you can try to kill me with the hammer and the clamps. But if I can get out of the leather bag then I will tie you up in the leather bag and try to kill you," he explained.

Trembling with rage and frothing at the mouth from continuous incomprehensible mutterings and mumblings, the old woman tied him up in the bag. Then she began to hit him with the hammer and pinch him with the clamps. But as the bag was so old it soon tore and the brother got out.

"Now it's your turn to get into the bag," said the brother.

The old woman, full of apprehension, reluctantly got into the bag. The brother tied the mouth of the bag securely. Then he began to hit her with the iron hammer and pinch her with the iron clamps. As the leather bag was new and strong, she could not get out, however hard she struggled. The old woman was not only hurt by the hammering and the pinching but also suffocating in the bag and she cried out hysterically. *"Nga pagung di nang la shi gi du. Nga pagung di nang la shi gi du* (l am dying in this leather bag. I am dying in this leather bag)" and indeed, she died. The brother and his sister could then live happily and in peace.

Chanting mantras in a serene and self-composed tone, he finally subdued the rolong.

Ap Rolong

Dangbo..o..o Dingbo..o..o.. there was a trader who lived with his wife and his daughter. He often made long trading trips to Tibet and India. Now it happened that he had to make a journey to India to replenish his stock of salt. He wanted to have his stock of salt in time for the rice harvest so that he could exchange it for grain which he would then take to Tibet and thereby increase his profits even further.

After days of preparations he was ready to start his journey. The pack mules were well fed and strong, and their saddles had been repaired or replaced as needed. His food provisions were packed and his little tent was folded neatly and ready. Then he counted out his silver coins and was satisfied. He was sure he would have a successful trade. He bade farewell to his wife and daughter and began his journey southwards to India.

As the days passed the rice was harvested and eaten or bartered but the trader did not return. Days grew into months and still he did not come. As more time passed the mother and her daughter became increasingly concerned. They were now quite convinced that something terrible had happened to him. The trader had made meticulous preparations for his journey but in those days there was nothing he could do to prevent himself from contracting the fatal *satpa* or malaria which killed many people from the highlands when they dared to descend to the heavily forested plains where malaria was endemic. The *satpa* had killed him too.

One evening all the dogs in the village started to wail and howl in the most strange way and soon the mother and daughter could hear the father calling for them, but from the way the dogs barked, they knew that it was only his *rolong* or his corpse that had revived after death and was possessed by a malevolent spirit. So they hid in the roof truss. The father tried to come into the house but as he was only a *rolong* he could neither bend his head nor lift his feet to cross the threshold and he kept on banging his head against the beam above the door and hitting his feet against the threshold. After a long time he was finally able to stumble into the house. The two women had to hold their hands over their mouths to prevent themselves from screaming on seeing the *rolong* in front of them. For what they saw was a horrific image of the man they used to know and love. There stood an ash-gray naked man with his eyes fallen deep into their sockets. His nose was bare bone, and there was no flesh over his gums. His hair stood on end. They scrutinized him from head to toe. There were mustard flowers between his toes which must have been caught there as he shuffled through the mustard fields near the village. His movements were slow, stiff and awkward as his joints were locked in rigor mortis. Once in the house he began to look for his wife and daughter everywhere. He went to the fireplace and blew into the embers to start a fire but only maggots fell out of his mouth, for a *rolong* has no breath. It is said that *rolongs* will try to transform as many living human beings into *rolongs* as possible. They can do this by simply touching the human beings on the head. He began to search the house for his wife and his daughter, but before he could find them the roosters in the village cried, "*Cockerico, cockerico, cockerico,*" and he left, for *rolongs* become simple corpses after the first cock crow. As he left the house he muttered, "Let's say that you won today."

The mother and daughter worried the whole day because they knew that he would come again. As darkness fell the dogs started to bark in that strange way again and sure enough he came. The mother and daughter hid under a pile of nine *zangs* or huge water storage containers which were turned upside down, one on top of the other. The *rolong* seemed to struggle for a long time to get into the house but when he did he headed for the pile of *zangs* and in his awkward slow movements, he began to turn them up one by one. Before the last *zang* could be turned the village rooster called, "Cockerico, cockerico, cockerico," and the *rolong* had to leave again, muttering angrily, "Let's say you won again."

The next evening they hid under nine layers of baskets. The *rolong* came and turned up the baskets one by one but before he could turn the last basket the first rooster called and they were saved once again. Now the mother and daughter were terrified, for they knew that he would not leave them until he had transformed them into *rolongs*. So they decided to run away. They carried whatever belongings they could carry and left the village quietly so as not to raise an alarm. On the way they happened to meet an old ragged *chodpa*. They stopped to talk with him and when he asked them why they were leaving the village, they told him the whole story. The *chodpa* explained to them that the *rolong* would follow them wherever they went so it was no use running away. He advised them that as long as the *phowa* rites to release his *namshi* or spirit from his body were not performed there was no way of getting away from a *rolong*. He said that even if the body of a *rolong* were chopped up into pieces and scattered in different places or cremated it could always come together again. He offered to come with them and to perform the rites if they were willing to return to their home. The *chodpa's* quiet knowledge and his unassuming and gentle manners won the confidence of the fugitives. They placed full faith in the *chodpa* and returned home with him.

On arrival in the village the *chodpa* instantly began to make preparations. He gathered some pieces of bamboo, heated them over the fire, and then cut them into splinters. He also asked for some *naktha* or rope made of yak hair. As darkness fell, he began to perform the **chod**. Soon the dogs began to bark as usual and the *rolong* came calling for his wife and daughter. The *chodpa* confronted him and started to beat him with the *kangdom* or thigh-bone trumpet, all the time reciting the mantras of the *chod*. A most frightening struggle ensued. For a long time the two women feared that the *chodpa* would succumb to the persistent iron-like grip of the *rolong*, who seemed to experience neither pain nor exhaustion. Sweat poured down the *chodpa's* brow but he would not give up. Chanting the mantras in a serene and self-composed tone, he finally subdued the *rolong*. He pinned him down on the floor. He placed his right knee on the *rolong's* chest and his left on the floor. Then he blew into the thigh-bone trumpet triumphantly three times. He then drove the bamboo splinters into all the joints of the *rolong's* body and tied it up with the *naktha* as a corpse would normally be tied up for cremation. He administered the *phowa* rite on the corpse, chanting the mantras and clicking his fingers as he repeated, "Phad...phad". The spirit of the dead was now freed and no longer vulnerable to the malevolent spirits which had lived within his body.

The woman and her daughter could now live in peace without fear and regret, for the *rolong* was subdued and the deceased had received the appropriate death rites.

Lame Monkey

Dangbo..o..o Dingbo..o..o.. there was a poor woman who had a son who was big and strong but quite worthless. He could spend all his days just lying in a meadow and watching the clouds drift in the sky or he would sometimes sit on the steps of the village chorten or stupa and watch the village children as they played in the archery ground. He was so lazy that he would not even raise his hand up to his nose to clean it. The villagers nicknamed called him Pladong or Lazy.

Year after year while the other villagers busied themselves with the processes of plowing, planting, and harvesting, life for Pladong was unchanging. Every morning he rose when the sun was high in the sky and went to lie down again in the meadows after he had eaten what his mother had prepared. He had spent eighteen years of his life doing absolutely nothing.

Pladong's neighbor was a kindly old man who was always ready to help the mother and son. One year he sternly said, "This will never do, Pladong. You have to start doing something." He gave Pladong a *dri* of maize seeds and showed him how to prepare the field and sow them. Every day Pladong resentfully followed the kind old man to the field who taught him all he knew. Pladong finally learned to work and he was happy when the maize field was full of tall plants with rich big cobs, full of the promise of a rich harvest. Every day he went to check his field to see when it would be ready for harvesting. Finally it was time for harvest! So early one morning when he went to the field, carrying the largest basket he could find in the house, he was dreaming of the rows upon rows of golden cobs that would fill the attic of his house. His dream was abruptly ended when he saw with shock that his entire field was

The king not only wept openly but personally came with a **katar** *to see the monkey and to pay homage to him.*

full of monkeys. They had eaten what they could and had played around by pulling the stalks this way and that way. Not a single maize cob was left in the field. Full of fury Pladong began to chase the monkeys but they ran into the nearby forest and quietly disappeared into the thick foliage of the trees. He lost all of them save for a lame monkey who could not run as fast as the others and was hiding behind a tree. He caught the monkey by its neck and threatened to kill it.

The monkey begged to be spared. "I will help you and make you a rich man if you will spare me my life."

"No, never!" said the boy, who was fuming with anger because the first useful thing he had ever done in his life had been thwarted by a group of mischievous monkeys.

"Kuchen la (mercy)," begged the monkey, "I promise you that I will make you a very rich man."

After many pleas and promises Pladong finally agreed to spare the monkey's life if he could indeed make him a rich man.

The monkey at once headed to the palace of the king of the region and stated boldly, "O king, the king of Bhakho needs a bride. Your daughter would make a fitting queen for the king."

The king stared at the monkey in utter disbelief. But being a king he quickly regained his royal composure and said, "Before I give my daughter away I must see the palace of your king."

"That can easily be arranged. I shall inform the king of Bhakho," replied the monkey as his mind began to work frantically on a scheme to get a palace for his king.

Next, the monkey went to the palace of the *sinpo* which was located in the next valley. The nine storeyed palace stood in the middle of a broad valley surrounded by rich fields of wheat and barley. Scores of cattle and horses grazed on the hillsides. The palace walls were richly decorated with precious metals and they shone and glittered in the sunlight. Seeing this the monkey thought, " Hummm ... this will make a fine palace for my king."

So the monkey limped confidently to the palace gate and was at once met by the one-eyed lady who was the gate keeper of the *sinpo's* palace.

"I carry with me an edict from the king of China and I must give it the *sinpo* himself this instant," announced the monkey.

The one-eyed lady looked severely at this monkey with her one eye and called the three-eyed guard. The three-eyed guard rolled its eyes menacingly in different directions and said, "Five Eyes will know what to do with you."

The guard with the five eyes came, and without even looking in his direction called the seven-eyed guard who came promptly and, taking one quick look at the monkey, said, "Go and meet the other Eyes," and pointed towards a series of doors. The monkey went in and met the guards with various numbers of eyes and finally Nine Eyes took him and ushered him into the presence of the *sinpo*, announcing, "The messenger from China."

The monkey at once took out a sheet of paper, and with an extravagant flourish, and holding himself as tall as he could possibly make himself, he cleared his throat three times and proceeded to read aloud the edict from the king of China. The edict simply said, "The king of China declares war on the *sinpo*."

The *sinpo* instantly fell into a state of panic and began to pace back and forth in his enormous room. His head hung over his chest and his fangs drooped and touched the golden floors, making deep furrows in the floor as he paced back and forth restlessly. "Do you know the king of China?" he at last addressed the monkey.

"Yes, I do, " lied the monkey effortlessly. "In fact I know him quite well," he added, when the *sinpo* did not respond.

When the *sinpo* still did not react he went on, "Now as I see that you are a good *sinpo*, I would also like to warn you that the king of China intends to use something called cannons on you."

"How can we save ourselves from the cannon?" asked the *sinpo*, suddenly interested.

The monkey replied, "That will be easy if you do exactly as I tell you."

The *sinpos* enthusiastically followed his advice. They immediately constructed straw huts. "The cannon balls will go right through the straw," the monkey had told them judiciously, "and you will all be saved."

When the huts were ready the monkey asked all the *sinpos* to get into the huts and warned them not to get out on any account until he told them to do so. Once the *sinpos* were all in the huts, the monkey lit a torch and went from hut to hut setting them on fire, one after the other, yelling "*Sinpo gola mai chop chop* (Fire on the sinpo)."

The *sinpos* shrieked, "Is it not time to get out yet?"

"These cannons are very powerful indeed. We are burning."

"We are being roasted alive." Soon only the ashes of the *sinpos* blew about in the wind and the lame monkey had got the most beautiful palace for the Bhakho king.

The Bhakho king now had to have some clothes worthy of his position. The monkey once again began to contrive a scheme. He went to the king's tailor and picked up all the discarded pieces of the richest fabrics he could find—there were brocades, silks, and velvets. Taking these he headed to the river and scattered them on the bushes that grew on the banks of the river. Having done this he told the Bhakho king to sit on a boulder in the middle of the river. Then he pretended to panic and rushed to the king and exclaimed, "The king of Bhakho was on his way to visit you and to personally invite you to his palace. Last night he camped on the river bank and a sudden flood washed away the entire camp and the king has lost everything. The only survivors were the king and myself."

"What can I do for your king?"

"The king needs some clothes as all his clothes were washed away and only a few pieces of cloth can be found scattered along the banks of the river," wailed the monkey, with the saddest expression on his face.

The king looked out of his window and it was indeed true, the bushes on the river banks were littered with bits and pieces of the richest fabrics as the Bhakho king sat naked and shivering on a boulder in the middle of the river. He at once asked his servants to send some of the best clothes in his palace to the disaster-stricken king of Bhakho. In this way the Bhakho king not only had the best palace but also the best clothes.

The king, accompanied by his ministers visited the palace and gasped at its wealth and grandeur. The palace was splendid and the wealth was enormous. He at once agreed to give his daughter as the bride. As the auspicious day of the wedding drew nearer the monkey realized with alarm that his king had never lived in a palace, eaten good food, nor had he been in the company of kings and princes, so he had to teach the Bhakho king to walk carefully on golden floors that shone and glittered. Most importantly he had to warn this hungry boy not to eat too quickly or too much.

On the day of the wedding the monkey limped beside the king and send subtle and discreet signs to his king to remind him to behave regally. Every time the Bhakho king walked carelessly and took steps that were too big, the monkey tugged his sleeve. When the Bhakho king began to eat too much the monkey made a fist at the king. Everybody who came to the wedding talked of nothing else for days afterwards but the young and handsome king who was so royal and so rich.

Thus, the Bhakho king and his queen lived happily together for many years while the lame monkey stayed on to advise them. The monkey as he grew older began to feel neglected and he often wondered whether the Bhakho king was grateful to him. He thus decided to test the king's memory and his gratitude. So one day he lay down under a tree, put some *kaphe* in his mouth, which looked like the eggs of meat flies, and pretended to be dead. It was not long before one of the servants saw him and went to report to the king, "O king, the monkey is dead."

"Well, what are you waiting for? Drag it by its legs and throw it into the river," said the king unconcernedly.

At this the monkey was absolutely infuriated and threatened the king, saying, "I shall tell everybody who you really are."

The king was mortified and begged the monkey for his forgiveness.

From then on the monkey was treated with respect and concern until a few years later, when again he felt neglected. He once again pretended to be dead. This time when the news of his death was reported to the king, the king not only wept openly but personally came with a *katar* to see the monkey and to pay homage to him. This made the monkey very happy and he had a great urge to laugh. While he was trying to suppress his laughter he choked on the *kaphe* which he had sprinkled in his mouth and he indeed died.

Finally they saw an old woman sitting by herself in the middle of a forest and busily frying something in a pan.

Gangze Joy Guma

Dangbo..o..o Dingbo..o..o.. there was an old couple who had a son. The son was a very lazy man. He was apathetic and passive towards everything. He had not done a day's work in his entire life except to come into the house to eat his meals and sleep and then go out and lie in the sun day after day. The aging parents worried endlessly about their only son. "How will he fend for himself after we are gone?" they asked themselves, and shook their heads sadly.

One fine day they had a plan to get him interested in doing something for himself. They thought that perhaps every time the boy was rewarded for his deeds he would be encouraged to do more work.

One day the father hung a basket of meat from a branch in a tree not far from the house. Soon a bevy of ravens began to caw excitedly around the tree

The father pretended to be very curious and said, "Son, there seems to be something on the tree. Why don't you go and have a look?"

But the boy was not at all interested and did not go willingly. He shuffled along as if his feet weighed heavily and walking was an annoyance. When he reached the tree and saw the basket of meat hanging on a branch of the tree, he at once cut the rope and carried home the meat. The parents, of course, pretended to be very happy and grateful to him. Another time the father hid a roll of butter in the leaves and when the cat began to scratch up the leaves the boy went and found the roll of butter which the parents once again enthusiastically received. The parents kept on hiding things and praising the son when he brought home whatever he happened to

133

find. Now the boy began to become ambitious and confident of himself. He wanted to do something great in his life.

When the son was twenty-five years old he asked his parents to give him a pipe that measured nine *du* or hand spans and a sword that was as large as eighteen arm spans. The son then set out, with the pipe in his mouth and armed with the sword, and began to clean up the forests on the hills as if the energy stored in his body for all these years had to come out in some form. The father begged him to go and find something more worthwhile to do. With the pipe sticking out in front of him and the sword, which he carried upright, towering far above his head he left his parents' home and went in search of people who would match his own strength and ambition. He walked on for many days until he saw a man who was busy breaking boulders from a hill. The pipe-smoking hero, as he was now called, just watched him. The boulder-breaking man turned to him and said "I am Bjah Phomi, the boulder-breaking hero, who are you?"

"I am *Gangze Joy Guma*, I smoke this nine-*du* pipe."

They at once became friends and decided to travel together. Soon they saw a man standing in the middle of a river and stopping the river's flow with the incredibly huge calves of his legs. The pipe-smoker and the boulder-breaker asked him who he was and he said:

"I am Bjimtha Chu Chemi, the hero who stops the river with his calves."

He became the third friend and they traveled all over the place performing their preposterous exploits until one day the pipe-smoker ran out of tobacco. They then went in search of tobacco everywhere. Finally they saw an old woman sitting by herself in the middle of a forest and busily frying something in a big frying pan. First Bjah Phomi went to her and asked her if she could tell him where they could find some tobacco. Without even taking the time to look up at the hero she just pulled him down with one hand as she continued to fry whatever she was frying and stuck him under her left knee. She was frying human nails. Then Bjimtha Chu Chemi ran up to her but she pulled him down too, with her right hand, and stuck him under her right knee. Then *Gangze Joy Guma* went up to the woman, turned over the frying pan, and took the largest burning log from the fire. He held her down by putting his left hand on the nape of her neck and scorched her to death with the burning log of wood. He released his friends. This demonstration of superior strength was sufficient to win the unfailing loyalty and allegiance of the other heroes. *Gangze Joy Guma* was the undisputed champion, the strongest and the bravest of them all.

Nearby was the splendid house of the dead witch. They decided to live in the house. One day when they opened the innermost door of the house they found a beautiful girl whom the witch had locked up. *Gangze Joy Guma* married her. Now the strongest hero was served by two other heroes, and they lived together very happily and their lives continued to be one fantastic saga of adventure after adventure.

Before the woman realized what was happening the stick came towards her and began to beat her up mercilessly.

The *Phob* that Provided Food

Dangbo thik naki wenda dingbo thik naki wenda ... there stood a village in a wide river valley. The valley bottom was covered with rich fields of yellow and golden barley ready for harvest. The hillsides were all dug and prepared for the buckwheat to be sown. Soon everybody would be busy sowing buckwheat except the poor boy who lived in the rundown old shack of a house ... he was simply too poor to have kept enough seeds, he had eaten every grain in the house. Seeing the plight of this poor boy all the neighbors collected a handful of seeds for him and he gratefully sowed them in his little patch of land located on the hillside near a pine forest.

As soon as the seeds were sown a big family of sparrows came and, twittering and fluttering, they picked up every grain within a short while as the poor boy watched helplessly, paralyzed with shock. Slowly the initial shock gave way to intense anger and he began to chase the sparrows. He found the nest of the sparrows in a thorny bush, and inside there were six helpless chicks. Boiling with anger he was about to set them on fire when the sparrows begged him to spare their lives. The boy said, "What will I live on now that you have eaten my seeds? I cannot spare your lives." The father sparrow gave him a *phob* and said, "With this *phob* you do not have to do a day's work, whatever you want will come out of the *phob*." So the boy took the *phob* and went home.

It was true, the *phob* produced rich and delicious meals for the poor boy every day, any time he asked it. As the boy no longer went to beg for scraps of food from his rich neighbor's house, the *mailiama* or matriarch of that household became very suspicious. One day she went to see how the poor boy was feeding himself. As she watched him, he took a fairly worn out *phob* from the pouch of his

137

gho and put it in front of him. Then he said, "Today I would like a very rich meal. I would like to have rice and meat. Use red rice and give me *singchang* to go along with the food."

Before she could blink her eyes the food was in front of the boy. The *bangchung* was filled with steaming red rice. The rice grains were so even and smooth, she had never seen the like before. The *dapa* was filled with juicy pieces of pork, beef, tripe, and sausages, with large red and green chilies, and tender slices of radishes. The meal appeared as if it had just been cooked. The boy began to eat the food without a hint of surprise. He ate the meal with a great smacking of his lips and then held up the ornately decorated *bamairuchung* and poured himself a cup of the coolest and clearest *singchang* she had ever seen. The woman decided at once that she had to have the magical *phob*. She began to plan how she could possibly get it from him. She asked the poor boy to run an errand to the next valley, together with her son. As they had to cross numerous gorges and ravines to reach the next valley, they would be away for a few days. So the woman and her son went to the poor boy and in her sweetest voice, which was full of feigned concern, she told him that she would keep the *phob* with her for safe keeping while he was away.

After some days the boys returned from their trip and the woman gave the *phob* back to the poor boy. What she had actually done was to keep the magical *phob* for herself and give him another *phob* which was very like it. The poor boy went home and asked for a good meal but nothing came out of the *phob* even though he repeated the request several times. The poor boy became very angry and went straight to the sparrow and demanded to know why he had been cheated. This time the sparrow gave him a kid, saying, "Every time you wash and pat the kid you will get enough money to buy food for a long time."

The poor boy washed and patted the kid as soon as he reached home and sure enough pieces of silver and gold coins fell from its body. Once again the woman became curious and went to find out how the poor boy was getting his money. When she saw the kid goat she wanted it. She once again succeeded in replacing the kid goat with a false one. When the false kid goat failed to produce any coins the poor boy headed straight to the sparrow and asked for something else. The sparrow said, "You did not look after the gifts very well and that's how you lost them. Now I have nothing else but this stick, but it may be useful, so take it and never come back for I have repaid you adequately."

The poor boy was now crestfallen and asked, "What can I do with a stick?"

"Place the stick on your altar revere it, and make three prostrations towards it and it will beat up anybody you ask it to."

The boy went home with the stick and soon the mother of the rich boy was in his house asking him what the stick could be used for. By now the poor boy had guessed who had taken his *phob* and his kid so he said, "If you can wait for a while I can show you what it can do."

The woman could barely contain her excitement as she watched the boy complete the prostrations to the stick. The boy then gave a command. Before the woman realized what was happening the stick came towards her and began to beat her up mercilessly. She ran out of the house but the stick chased her wherever she went. Stumbling and falling repeatedly, she eventually was able to stammer, "I sub...submit, I sur...rend...er, I have ta...ken the *phob* and the ki...kid. But I will return them to you im...im...mediately."

"Ya, ya, in that case, stop stick!" ordered the boy.

The woman ran to her house and brought back the stolen goods and with folded hands begged the poor boy never to set the stick after her again. Now the poor boy had all the three gifts of the sparrow and he lived in happiness and prosperity without having to do a day's worth of work.

Part 2
Legends

Demons and Demonesses

It is said that Buddha Drukpa Kinlay, one of Tibet's foremost saints and an enlightened Master of Tantrism, came to Bhutan and traveled widely, successfully subjugating various demons and demonesses in Bhutan. We are told that the saint did not go beyond Pele La, which is the pass in the chain of mountains that divides the country into east and the west. The demons and the demonesses on the eastern side of the Pele La thrive and prosper to this day. How this came about is told in the following story. The lama happened to be traveling in the Pele La region one day. When he arrived at the pass he could not decide whether he should go further east from there or not. Just then an old man carrying a heavy load came along. Drukpa Kinlay asked this old man what villages he would find down in the valley. The old man replied, "First Rukhubji, then Chendibji, and then Tangsbji."

At this the saint, in his usual facetious way, said, "I don't think I will go to the valley of the three *bjis*" and returned the way he had come.

Thus the demons and demonesses on the eastern side of Pele La escaped Drukpa Kinlay's subjugation. Famous among the demonesses is the dermo or demoness of Nyala Lungma.

Garba Lung Gi Khorlo sped down to the Mangdi river.

Garba Lung Gi Khorlo and the Demoness of Nyala

We are told that the Tongsa *penlops* or the governors of Tongsa were more or less able to maintain effective control over Tongsa and the surrounding regions even while the other governors were engaged in continuous power struggles among themselves for supremacy. Thus, the post of Tongsa *penlop* was not only prestigious but also very important. Young aspirants from all over the country yearned to be in the service the Tongsa *penlop*. These courtiers and attendants were said to be the brightest and the best. The elders tell us that a certain Tongsa *penlop* enjoyed the services of two truly remarkable men. They were his personal attendants or *garbas*. *Garba Lung gi Khorlo*, which translates as "attendant with wheels of wind", was one of them. He was said to have been an exceptionally fast walker and, therefore, an excellent courier. He could walk so fast that he almost flew. Penjor was the other *garba*, and he was an extraordinarily fast tailor. He was the *penlop's* tailor and could hand-sew a *gho* in one day, an incredible feat in those days when hand-sowing a *gho* usually took more than two whole days. The *penlop* was very proud of these two men and they were always expected to do a lot.

Garba Lung gi Khorlo had to carry messages every day and he had never let down his master. It is said that he could travel from Tongsa to Wangdiphodrang and back in a day. This journey is about 129 kilometers through rugged craggy terrain and would usually take an average person at least four days.

Those were the days of factions, conspiracies, and plots. A single strong man had yet to emerge and the regional lords were constantly feuding, intriguing and scheming against each other. It was of the utmost importance that allies kept contact with each other and expediting information across the rugged terrain was crucial but at the same time a very big challenge. *Garba Lung gi Khorlo's* services to the penlop were invaluable. But *Garba Lung gi Khorlo's* real moment of victory came not so much from the distance he covered or the speed with which he completed his feat but when he was standing in the presence of his master and receiving the usual impassive *"Tubay"* or "alright".

One day the *penlop* had a message of great urgency which had to be conveyed to the Wangdi *dzongpon* immediately. The penlop knew that he could rely on his attendant. The Zimpon handed the letter to *Garba Lung gi Khorlo* and conveyed the penlop's order for him to speed to the Wangdi *dzongpon* and bring back the reply the same day. As *Garba Lung gi Khorlo* left the *penlop's* court the tailor was just unfolding a fabric for a *gho*. It was at the hour of the first cock crow.

Garba Lung gi Khorlo sped down to the Mangdi river and climbed to the other side of the Tongsa ravine and was soon climbing towards Pele La. He had done this trial many times and each turn and every ascent was familiar to him. But each journey now caused him more apprehension. It was no longer a challenge and a test of his own prowess as it used to be in the earlier days. Each journey took more and more energy and effort. The soles of his feet hurt and his calves burnt as if there was fire in them and his thighs grew heavier. Above all he dreaded the day he would fail his master, the day that his master would not say *"Tubay"*. As he thought of all these changes in himself he passed through Nyala Lungma and he soon passed by the Nyala *dermo's phodrang* or palace—which is in rather an inconspicuous place not much different from the rest of the region. It is a small shaded ravine in the oak forest, it is dark, and hardly any sunlight reaches the place and it is wet although there is no stream anywhere. The most striking feature of this place is that it has an eerie atmosphere and you always feel that uncanny presence of someone that you cannot see. In a moment of impulsive reckless he looked towards the demon's abode and shouted, "I am tired, I am so tired that I would rather you took my life than that I do one more journey like this."

Soon after midday he was in the court of the Wangdi *dzongpon* and after a quick meal he was ready and on his way back with the reply for the Tongsa *penlop*. By early evening he was already approaching Nyala Lungma and was looking forward to the rest at the end of his journey. He took comfort in the thought that his wife would be waiting with a good meal and strong *ara* at his home in Tongsa. There were no human settlements anywhere in the area although he occasionally met one or two people on the way. They were sometimes travelers like himself, herders, or pilgrims. He would greet them and ask them a few questions but never stopped to actually talk with anyone. But today it was different and he had to stop and look carefully. For there was a woman wearing the region's famous *tarichem kira* which is a black woolen *kira* with bands of red and blue. She was bending towards a little stream and washing a basket of meat. A closer look revealed that the basket contained what looked like entrails of some fairly large animal. The woman was completely preoccupied. She had her back towards the road and was bending down towards the water trough and washing the contents of the basket. *Garba Lung gi Khorlo* wondered how it was possible that in the middle of nowhere there was this woman washing meat. So he asked, "It looks like a big animal. Is your cow herd nearby?" The woman continued to wash the meat and did not turn to answer him. She simply said, "This is not an animal's entrails. *Garba Lung gi Khorlo* gave me his life this morning. These are his entrails." As if in a dream she then disappeared, leaving not a trace of her having ever been there. The emptiness and the silence seemed to envelop him, a shudder ran down his spine, and his skin rose in goose pimples. He seemed to float for the rest of his journey. He had no thoughts or pain, he just felt a lightness in his being.

The conch shell was being blown from the monastery to mark the end of the day as he entered the Tongsa *dzong*. Darkness had fallen and one could no longer read the lines of the palm of the hand. He felt a sense of calm and satisfaction but there was a sadness that transcended everything. He saw that the tailor had completed stitching a *gho* that he had cut out in the morning and was folding it. *Lung gi Khorlo* did not stop to greet any one, he went straight into the inner chambers of the court and presented the letter of the Wangdi *dzongpon* to the Tongsa *penlop*. The *penlop* seemed to have a trace of a smile on his face and there was perhaps a hint of emotion when he said, "*Tubay*". The *penlop* then pointed to a large bowl of rice on which were placed a generous portions of dried meat and a large roll of butter. A servant stepped out nimbly from behind the *gochor* or screen in front of the door, picked up the gifts, and indicated to *Garba Lung gi Khorlo* that the audience was over. The two men then stepped backwards until were behind the *gochor* and left the *penlop* to read the letter. *Garba Lung gi Khorlo* had once again not failed his master. He went home, quietly ate his meal, and followed it with a cup of delicious strong *ara*. As he ate his meal he calmly related the incident to his wife. After the meal he lay down, asleep and never woke up again.

Any one traveling the lateral highway across Bhutan has to pass through Nyala Lungma. It is the area between Chendibji and Thumbidrak. It is always dark and always a little damp. There is no abode in the true sense of the word. But the demon lives here somewhere. Once you have heard this legend the place seems almost forbidding. Do stop and remember her, for she appreciates acknowledgment but do not call upon her to do anything. One can never sure; she might just take you seriously.

Yirang Pamo's Visit to the House of Nyala Dermo

It is believed that even spirits and demons are afflicted with pain and disease like human beings. We are told that sometimes the spirits seek the help of human beings to cure their sick and afflicted.

Yirang Pamo Lhamo was a very powerful Bumthangpa *pamo* or shaman medium. Although she came from Yirang which is in the Tang Block of Bumthang district the fame of her power and skill had reached far and wide and she would be called upon to perform rituals in faraway places like Thimphu or even Paro. It happened once while she was making the long journey from Yirang to Thimphu that she had to spend a night somewhere near Nyala Lungma. Genuine and powerful *pamos* are recognized and even respected by spirits and demons, and being aware of this, they are therefore not afraid of anything. So when a beautiful woman appeared from nowhere out of the forest and asked her to help her she agreed without fear.

This beautiful woman avoided eye contact and always looked away when she spoke. "My son is very sick, I would be grateful if you could look at him. Perhaps there is something that you can do to help him."

They walked in silence for a while through the forest. Deep in the forest of oak and conifers, far away from all human habitation there suddenly appeared a magnificent house. The *pamo* went in and was shown the patient who was lying on a mat on the floor. The patient, a young man, was covered with sores. After a quick look the *pamo* realized that the sores were full of mustard seeds. She at once knew

The pamo *turned to take another look at the beautiful cow and found herself staring stupidly at a huge rat that was pulling and struggling at the rope.*

what had happened. When human beings are afflicted with sicknesses caused by the ill will of spirits and demons, *choepas* perform the ritual of *kago*. During this ritual mustard seeds are thrown at the patient to symbolically chase away the spirits. Here was proof that the good *choepas* in fact made effective contact with the unseen harmful beings and actually injured them.

Unlike other times when the *pamo* contacts malevolent spirits, bargains, and negotiates with them, in this case all that she could do was to call upon the human guardian deities and ask for forgiveness. When she had completed the rituals she was led out of the house. As she was passing through the rooms she recognized a man from Bumthang. He was wearing an unmistakable Bumthang *matha* and was bending intently over a pile of sewing placed in front of him. She stopped and looked at him carefully, hoping that he would see her, but he would not look up from his work. The *pamo* recognized the man as Kencho, the late husband of Nimalung *Animo*. He had died some months ago and now was a *khor* or bondaged spirit slave of the **dermo**.

Here is what had happened to Kencho before he died and became a *khor*. He was returning from Thimphu and had to spend a night in a cave somewhere near Nyala Lungma. Throughout that night there was a tremendous wind that roared ceaselessly and it hailed and rained tumultuously. On this fearful night Kencho gratefully submitted to the lure of a beautiful woman who had mysteriously appeared from nowhere and befriended him in his cave.

Several days after his return to Nimalung, he fell seriously ill and, after many months of intense suffering, finally died. It was believed that Nyala *dermo* had taken his *sog* or life force on that fatal night in the cave. The *pamo* Lhamo had in fact been called upon to help him in his last days but it was too late. She had told the relatives and his wife that a demon had bound him nine times with a chain, never to be released. Kencho had become a bondaged spirit slave to the Nyala demoness.

On seeing the plight of Kencho the *pamo* was filled with compassion and she regretted that she had not been able to help him. With these thoughts going through her mind she happened to linger a little, at which the dermo who was leading her out of the house turned back impatiently and her face darkened. The *pamo* quickened her pace and followed her out of the house. The *dermo* handed her a rope tied around the horns of a beautiful milking *jatsam* and curtly said, "This is in return for your services" and instantly disappeared. The *pamo* turned to take another look at the beautiful cow and found herself staring stupidly at a huge rat that was pulling and struggling at the rope.

Nyala *dermo's* life had once again impinged on the life of human beings.

The *Ani* and the *Migoi*

Dangbo..o..o Dingbo..o..o.. past the deep forest, clinging onto the rocks on the side of the mountain was a cluster of five huts which were occasionally used by meditators as a hermitage. It now happened that one year an *ani* or nun was the sole occupant of these huts. She lived in the smallest hut, the one closest to the stream. She had undertaken to do the *losum chosum* meditation of three years of absolute isolation. The lonely days turned to lonelier months but after the first nine months of sheer loneliness she suddenly began to experience blissful tranquillity. She then no longer felt the pangs of hunger that so tormented her in the initial days. She ate a little flour and drank the butterless tea once a day more as a daily ritual than as a means to quench her hunger and her thirst. Her mind was at peace and she radiated peace and tranquillity.

It was her third winter by herself. She was no longer afraid of anything for she had overcome every kind of fear. So it was a sense of curiosity that was stirred when she heard a tremendous sound of heavy thumping and shuffling. The sound was accompanied by a very strong smell that nearly choked her. She waited in quiet anticipation as the sound drew closer to her hut and the smell became stronger. All at once a heavy shadow fell across the room and then suddenly there was an enormous effort of something being pushed through the window. The little room in which she sat became dark as the window was filled with the bulk of some strange creature's leg. Her little hut actually shook under its weight. It was a leg that looked like no other leg. It was something between a human leg and an animal leg. It was about two times the size of a yak leg and it was covered with fur. The fur was of a dark color but because of the

Her meditation was senseless if this creature was to continue to take the lives of other creatures for her sake.

darkness the exact color was difficult to tell. It was with serene composure that the *ani* wondered what she should do. Then as her eyes adjusted to the partial darkness she saw that a large bamboo stake had pierced the foot right through and was still stuck there. There was some blood and pus in the fur around the piece of bamboo. She saw that the creature was in need of help and this was its way of seeking it. The *ani* took her penknife and then tried to extract the bamboo. After a long period of labor, covered in perspiration, and dizzy from the foul smell of the creature, she was finally able to get the stake out. It was about a foot long. She then took some *gnymar* or sanctified butter and applied it lavishly to the wound. After a while the strange leg was withdrawn through the window with as much effort as when it was pushed in. Slowly the great mass of the creature moved away with a heavy thumping and crashing noise. With the fading noise the strong smell died away too. The *ani* felt a shudder down her spine as she wondered aloud, "Perhaps that was a *migoi*".

From then on, as if to thank the *ani*, the strange creature kept coming back to the hut bringing with it different kinds of game. The carcasses of deer, wild boar, birds, and other animals were regularly shoved through the window. It is said that the *ani* was greatly disturbed by these occurrences. Her meditation was senseless if this creature was to continue to take the lives of other creatures for her sake. So she had to move away to another hermitage to complete the meditation.

He knew at once that this must be what the old timers had warned him against, a migoi.

The *Zah* Collector and the *Migoi*

Dangbo..o..o Dingbo..o..o.. many years ago there was a man. Nobody really knew where he came from but everybody knew that he used to wander in the wild mountains of Bhutan and collect *zah*. He would collect as many as he could get and then go to Wongker in the Lhunsti district and sell them to a master wood-turner who turned these shapeless and ugly fungal growths of wood into beautiful and priceless *zahphi* cups and bowls. He had been to all the mountains over the years searching out and collecting *zah*. Like a hunter seeking out an animal he had sought out *zah*, and like a hunter thrilled at the final kill, he too could feel a thrill each time he carved out a burl from a tree.

Now it happened that he was on Sibshiri mountain in the Tang valley of Bumthang. He had with him his bags of food provisions and his precious bundle of *zah* which he had carefully carved out from the trees. Besides his axe and knife he had a matchlock, for life in the remote forest among the wild animals was dangerous.

It was winter, and it was bitterly cold. The fresh soft snow that fell continuously made walking impossible. With every step he would sink into it up to his waist. So he had taken shelter in a cave and he was getting restless as the ground continued to lie under a thick blanket of snow. All he could do was to wait for a change in the weather. For most of the day he sat in the cave warming himself by a fire and smoking his *gangza* or pipe. It was on such a day that there was a terrible blizzard, worse than any he had ever before experienced. The snowflakes fell out of the dark sky without a break, the wind roared and howled and swayed the trees mercilessly as if it would break them or blow them away. This continued for a long time. Suddenly the *zah* collector heard a terrible wailing, more piercing than the roar of the wind. The wailing which seemed to be full of pain and anguish sounded as if it were coming closer to him. While he strained his ears to listen to the sound more carefully, for each wail was followed by a long period of silence, a waft of the most foul smell reached his nostrils. He held his breath, for the smell was so strong that he grew dizzy with it. He kept his eyes focused on the wide entrance of the cave and thought hopelessly of the impossibility of protecting himself. Then suddenly he saw a dark shadow fall across the space in front of him and wafts of the foul smell reached him even more strongly now. As he sat there defenseless, he could hear the loud thumping of his own heart and his chest felt constricted. Impulsively he stood up suddenly. Perhaps he thought he could run away before the mysterious enemy came to him. He felt light headed, and the next moment his knees gave way and he crumpled on the floor of the cave, unconscious.

He was not sure how long he had lain in this state, but when he opened his eyes the huge entrance of the cave seemed partially blocked and streaks of faint light came into the cave around an enormous object that sat before him looking at him curiously with its beady eyes. He knew at once that this must be what the old timers had warned him against, a *migoi*. He studied this creature as it sat there in front of him. It was at least three times the length of an average man and about the breadth of a huge yak. Its body was covered with brown and black fur which was long in some places and short in others. Its feet and hands resembled those of a large monkey, its beady blue-black eyes were fixed on him. By now the smell had filled the cave and the *zah* collector's lungs were about to burst as he tried to control his breath.

Neither of them moved. They just sat there facing each other. The creature seemed to scrutinize the man, whose mind had now gone blank. After a long time, in a moment of restless uncertainty he took his *gangza*, filled it with tobacco, and lit it. The creature watched him quizzically. He had smoked a puff or two when the creature gestured for it. The man suddenly had an idea which he thought might be his only way to escape from certain death. With slow but deliberate movements he reached for his matchlock, all the time keeping his eyes fixed on the strange creature. He then filled it with gun powder as he had filled his pipe with tobacco and handed it to the *migoi*, which reached out and grasped it with hands as skillful as human hands. With the same proficiency this creature thrust the barrel of the gun into its mouth. The man then withdrew a burning piece of wood from the fire and lit the gun as the creature greedily sucked at it. Suddenly there was a flash of sparks and a muffled bang and the creature fell backwards. The man took one deep breath and ran to the entrance of the cave, and took one last look at the enormous thing which lay there like a huge pile of manure in the cave. He thought the head was severed from the body, but he could not be certain for he did not pause to take a second look. It did not even occur to him to check the hollow in its back in which it allegedly carried away human children whom it had stolen. He trudged through the snowstorm, stumbling and falling, without direction; he moved on, simply glad to be out of the cave and the danger. He did not know how long he traveled or even how he traveled but he reached the village of Tachiling which is nearly at the bottom of the Sibshiri, like a feverish man in delirium. The people took him in and sat him next to the fire. It was only after they had fed and nourished him with hot rich meals, together with strong *ara* warmed with butter and eggs, that he was finally able to tell them of his encounter with a *migoi*.

It is commonly believed that during unusually heavy snow the abominable snowman is driven down to lower altitudes. It is at such times that encounters with this otherwise elusive creature are experienced.

With the first light of day the men came out of their shacks in silence and sheepishly studied the blood-stained swords.

Mirgola

Mirgola are said to be human-like creatures that live in the depths of the remote forests in the Himalayas. They are not to be confused with the *migoi*, which are believed to be much larger than human beings and have a mystical aura of fear and wonderment associated with them. The *migoi* is known to the world as the elusive yeti or the abominable snowman. The *mirgola* on the other hand are less well known although there are many local stories about them. The existence of both the creatures is somewhat shrouded in mystery, and a sense of mythology and legend is evoked when reference is made to them. Yet many people in Bhutan are absolutely sure that these creatures do exist and that there is no question about that.

Today the forest of Somshid stands tall and thick, far away from human habitation. Nobody goes to this almost impregnable forest save the occasional herders who graze their cattle along the edges of the forest during part of the summer months. Somshid is located to the east of the Tang valley, and travelers to Kurtoi who cross the 4,100 meter (15,500 foot) Rodong La mountain pass near to it.

Many years ago the silence of the dark deep forest echoed with the sound of axes chopping the larch trees. A group of men had come to split wood to make shingles for a new roof for Ugen Choling *naktsang*. The men had been at their jobs for many days now. They worked hard during the day and they were so tired that in spite of the cold they slept soundly through the night. Now it happened that one morning when the men got up to start their work they were surprised to see that all the piles of shingles that they had made on the previous day had been shifted to different locations. They wondered what had happened and they grew apprehensive about the incident. Although none of them admitted it they were frightened by the strange happening. They wondered if this was a sign of the displeasure of the deities of the locality, whose wrath they might have incurred by cutting down the trees. If this was the case then they knew that they could be in for a lot of trouble. To their increasing anxiety the same thing was repeated over several nights until they finally decided to stay up for the night and keep watch.

As usual the men ate their dinner around the camp fire and went to bed in the shacks made of shingles. But this night they were only pretending to sleep. Soon the camp fire was flickering away as no more wood was fed to the fire and eventually there was just a warm glow where the fire had once been.

There was partial moonlight and the men strained their eyes to look into the dark night. Full of curiosity and anticipation they waited to see what would come. It was not long before some of the men saw some shadows and movements. They alerted the others, who now carefully followed the gaze of the ones who had seen something. There seemed to be figures darting noiselessly back and forth. It was too dark to see anything clearly.

Every now and then the moon emerged from behind a large cloud and they could see that these figures actually looked like children. But they could also have been some kind of a monkey. They had long arms and shaggy bodies and stood upright. They had hair falling from their foreheads like a fringe. Their eyes shone through the darkness. Soon they busied themselves taking all the shingles from the piles that were already made and making new piles just as the men had done during the day. One creature held one end of the shingle while another held the other end and they moved the shingles with the dexterity of human beings. They worked quickly and steadily until all the piles had been removed and remade and then they disappeared quietly into the forest.

The men had watched the whole thing in silent fascination barely able to refrain from going closer to look at them. These creatures were surely not human beings but what were they? The men were greatly intrigued and for the next few days they talked of nothing else but the nocturnal visitors who devotedly came and performed their tasks night after night. The men soon noticed that these creatures actually engaged in mimicry, imitating the gestures and other behavior of the men.

The men were getting quite used to these strange creatures when one of them suggested that they could have some fun by playing pranks on the creatures. The others agreed. So the next day the men made wooden swords and staged a mock battle with each other. The whole day they repeated the game, knowing full well that the creatures were watching and learning. They pretended to stab, cut, and slash at each other. Then they exchanged the wooden swords for real swords and retired for the night.

As on the previous nights the creatures emerged from their hiding places in the forest as, soon as the camp fires flickered and dwindled. This night they did not go to the piles of shingles as they had done on the previous nights. They walked to where the swords were piled up and looked at them cautiously, circling the pile on the ground. They tilted their heads at curious angles to examine the strange things but none of them dared to touch any of the lethal tools that glinted in the moonlight. Then all caution was suddenly cast aside when one of the creatures picked up a sword and brandished it in the air as the men had done. One by one the others picked up the swords and held them above their heads, not quite sure of themselves. They held them close to their faces to study the alien tools. They began to swing them a little and point them at each other. Then suddenly they began to attack each other exactly as the men had done. But of course this time the swords were real. The men were horrified, for their innocent prank had gone too far. They ran out of their shacks shouting and waving their arms wildly. The creatures threw down the swords and scuttled away in the darkness and disappeared into the forest, never to be seen again.

With the first light of day the men came out of their shacks in silence and sheepishly studied the blood-stained swords lying around where they had hurriedly been dropped; there were smears of blood still fresh on the shingles. But there was not a single creature to be found, dead, alive, or wounded. They had disappeared, taking with them the secret of their existence. Many days later when the men returned to the village and related the incident to the villagers, the elders nodded confidently and said, "*Mirgola*, surely *mirgola*."

The Girl who was Swallowed by a Python

There is some debate among the elders as to where exactly this story actually took place. Some storytellers talk of the girl as being a Kurtoizam, a girl from Kurtoi while others talk of her as a Khengzam, a girl from Kheng. One thing, however, is clear and that is that the incident which is about to be related took place in a sub-tropical part of Bhutan where *bemchi* or pythons are known to inhabit the thick jungles. As most Kurtoipas today claim that there are no pythons in Kurtoi it is most likely that this incident took place somewhere in Kheng.

Now, people are known to venture into the jungles in search of food, both in times of plenty and in times of scarcity. In times of plenty they go to look for variety and in times of scarcity they are driven into the wild by hunger. There are mushrooms, ferns, orchids, tubers, and fruits to be had from the jungles. So it was not unusual for the petite eleven-year-old girl who lived in a village on the fringes of an enormous expanse of sub-tropical forest to carry her basket on her back, stick her sickle into her belt, and head for the jungle.

The vegetation was luxuriant and the undergrowth thick but the girl pushed into the jungle with the confidence of one who had done this many times before. She could see the tracks of the cattle and she followed them. As she walked on she continually had to push away the branches that got in her way and unhook the numerous thorns that caught on her clothes. She did not mind these trivial obstacles for already she could smell the mushrooms and see the tender ferns. She collected whatever she could see. She was even lucky enough to find some wonderful orchids which she could pick from a low-hanging branch.

She chose a fairly small log and sat down on it and immediately took the basket straps off her shoulders.

The Girl who was Swallowed by a Python

Now her basket was filling up and she began to feel its weight. She needed to rest for a while. She decided that after a good rest she would head for home. So she was very pleased when she soon come into a little clearing in the forest where she could rest. She searched around for a suitable place to sit. There were several logs lying around. She chose a fairly small log and sat down on it and immediately took the basket straps off her shoulders. Suddenly there was a violent movement and the log on which she was sitting on turned around. The last thing she saw before she was swallowed by the *bemchi* was her basket falling onto the ground and the ferns, mushrooms, and orchids being scattered around.

The next moment she felt that she was being lifted off the ground and being squeezed into a very thin and tight tunnel. It was like being jammed into a bag that was far too small. Complete darkness descended upon her and she could neither see nor move. This realization was followed by pain all over her body. Her shoulders and her pelvic bones felt as if they were being crushed. After a while she felt numb all over. The only sensation she felt was the pain of the sickle in her belt pressing against her.

She tried to reach for the sickle. But it was impossible as her arms were locked into position so tightly that no movement was possible. Then she realized that the bag in which she was trapped was being dragged along. The next instant one arm was released by some movement of the bag. She could actually move her arm towards the sickle in her belt and just about touch the tip of the handle with the tips of her fingers. Try as she might, she could not move her arm any further—it seemed to have been once again locked in this new position. She was a strong-willed girl and she knew that she had to make the effort to live. With total concentration, and gathering up all her fast-ebbing strength, she pushed her arm towards the handle, further and further until finally she managed to grasp it and hold onto it. Then she pulled it out from her belt ever so painstakingly, for any movement was restrained and difficult. There was only one thought in her otherwise dulled mind,

167

"I have to slit open this bag and get out." She dug the sickle tip into the side of the bag that was on the ground and held onto it as firmly as possible. As the bag dragged along she suddenly saw light again and her body was free of the pressing and crushing sensations that she had experienced just a little while ago. A great sense of relief overcame her but the next moment complete darkness descended upon her again and she was unconscious.

In the meantime her parents noticed her absence and began to get anxious. She was taking much longer than usual. So the mother called her two sons, the girl's older brothers, and asked them to go in search of her, for it was not unusual for children to wander too far into the jungle and lose their way.

The two boys had no difficulty in following her tracks. They quickly found the cluster of ferns from which she had collected some and the freshly disturbed soil from where she picked the mushrooms. These clues soon led them to the little clearing. Suddenly both boys stood still in their tracks, their bodies taut with alarm and caution, for within an arm's length was a gigantic python that seemed to be resting in the fork of a huge tree. Hardly daring to breathe they watched the creature. But something was strange, for the creature did not move and its head was drooping down towards the ground and its great body was as limp and flaccid as a rope. They took a few cautious steps to take a closer look when suddenly the body of their sister sprawled face down on the ground came into view. "*Ya lama, kesa kud na* (the worst has happened)" was all the older brother could say as he rushed towards his sister. The other brother stood transfixed, gaping and gulping, until the older brother called to say that their sister was still alive. When he reached her she had been turned over. She was covered with a slimy substance and her right hand still grasped the sickle so tightly that her knuckles showed white.

Immensely relieved, the boys saw that their sister was only unconscious and stiff all over as if in rigor mortis. But they could not understand what had happened until one of the brothers saw that the underside of the python was slit open along its entire length. They concluded rightly, as confirmed by their sister later, that she had driven her sickle into the body of the python and that it had slithered along and slit itself as she held the sickle in the ground.

The boys carried their sister home. She was bathed again and again in water with the leaves of the medicinal wormwood plant. But where the slimy substance had come in contact with the skin, blisters broke out which festered and became sores. The girl finally recovered after much care and *rimdoe*, or powerful health-restoring rites and rituals. The sores on her face, hands, arms, and legs remained on her for her entire life as a constant reminder of her terrible encounter in the forest.

As he lifted his arms to shield his eyes, he just got a glimpse of the great greenish white serpentine creature.

The Man who was Saved by a Dragon

Many Bhutanese traders and pilgrims have, since time immemorial, braved the perilous journey across the mountains every year into Tibet. Traders would load their mules and yaks with rice, chilis, *dey shog*, the famous Bhutanese handmade paper, and various other goods for barter and journey across the mountains for many days until they reached the Tibetan settlements of their choice. They went in groups of at least three to four men. They carried enough rations and other stocks and once they reached the Tibetan settlements it was with confidence that they would go directly to their *nyda* to rest and to have their animals fed. With the same assurance they could trade their goods in the markets and proudly load their mules and return home.

But the pilgrims were another sort of traveler. Many of them had only a vague knowledge of Tibet and even less about the perils of the long journey there. Many pilgrims are known to have perished during the journeys and yet faith and devotion drew them to the *choe gi densa*, the centers of religion. Armed with his *kesang khurshing*, two strong U-shaped cane sticks that act like a light basket for holding provisions, and his T-shaped stick, which served as both a walking stick and a stool to rest his load on, a pilgrim from Tang valley in the Bumthang district headed for the 5,316 meter (17,442 foot) high Monla Karchung pass one spring day many years ago.

This pilgrim was a disgruntled farmer who felt that he had to seek a *tsawa lama*, a root teacher and follow the path of dharma. When he announced his intention, his family members were shocked but none would try to stand in the way of someone who had decided to seek religion. His brothers ungrudgingly and quietly assumed the tasks that he had abandoned to prepare for the long journey to Tibet.

So one spring morning the family tearfully bade farewell to this departing member of their family. They stood near the bridge and watched him as he confidently walked on. The women members waved their scarves and sang, "*Alo*", the melancholic farewell melody, while the men shouted, "*Aoo Aoo*" After a while they could only see the heavy *kesang khurshing*, within which he had packed all he needed. All of them wished that he had some traveling companion. But this potential pilgrim had always retorted quoting the famous Tibetan saying, "where can there be salvation without suffering?"

As the days passed he came closer to the famous Monla Karchung. The majestic white giant stood before his eyes and it seemed to beckon him towards it. This young and healthy farmer, who was used to hard work and carrying heavy loads, did not suffer having to climb the steadily ascending mountain path as the altitude increased rapidly. The white snow glistened in the bright sun and the glare hurt his eyes. Every thing looked white and icicles hung from the rocks. The dwarf azalea shrubs which had been quite abundant lower down now disappeared and everywhere he looked there was snow that sparkled and glittered in the sun. It was so quiet and peaceful that he was naturally reminded of the purpose of his journey He took out his prayer beads, which an old uncle who was a *gomchen* had given him, and began to chant the sacred syllables of **Om Mani Padme Hung**. As he recited he tried to visualize the image of *Chenrezi* as his uncle the *gomchen* had taught him to do. Whenever he tried to visualize *Chenrezi* his mind wandered and he saw his parents and his brothers and sisters and he began to wonder what they were doing. At once he would correct himself and try to concentrate. This went on for a while.

Now he was close to the *labza*, the pass itself the saddle of the Monla Karchung, where the track crossing into Tibet is located. He decided that he would rest for a while at the *labza* and eat the *lazi*, the specially prepared food to be eaten at the *labza* which his mother had so lovingly packed. He was only a few paces away from the pile of rocks that marked the *labza* when there was suddenly a tremendous thunderous cracking, crushing, and roaring noise. Everything around seemed to rumble and tremble uncontrollably. Before the pilgrim realized what was happening he felt as if a mat was being pulled away from under his feet. Then he felt himself falling, falling into a deep hole. Remarkably he landed on something soft. It was pitch dark and he could see nothing. He could not even begin to guess where he was. He sat there petrified that something even more terrible would happen to him. In his mind he could hear a voice saying, "pray, visualize *Chenrezi*", but his untrained mind wandered and intense fear gripped him. He began to tremble and shake so violently that he had to hold onto something lest he fall off the object he was sitting on. Frantically he groped around with his hands until he caught hold of something shaggy that felt like the mane of a horse. But of course that was not possible, so he assumed it must have been some dried moss. He held on to it and chanted the syllables *Om Mani Padme Hung* loudly while his mind raced widely and he could hardly follow the trend of his own thoughts.

When he finally regained some of his composure he realized that all around him, in this pitch darkness, there was total silence. "I have to find out where I am," he thought. He released one hand from the moss and stretched out in one direction. His hand came in contact with nothing. But when he touched the ground the same soft uneven surface seemed to stretch endlessly. He repeated this exercise in all directions and it was the same. There was emptiness all around save for the ground on which he sat. Then he began to inch his way until he felt that there was a drop. He dangled his feet down from the level where he was sitting until the tips of his toes touched the ground. He slowly let himself down and felt the solid ground under his feet. He took a handful of soil from the ground just to make sure it was not an illusion. There was ground under his feet but where was he? Was it a bad dream from which he would wake up?

A sense of sheer hopelessness enveloped him and tears of frustration stung his eyes and he cried out loudly. His cries echoed through what he now guessed was a deep cave. He sat crouched on the floor hugging his knees, not knowing what to do.

He did not know how much time had passed, he would never know. He began to explore a little, groping and falling in the darkness but always came back to the object on which he had fallen. By now he had come to depend on this object as a landmark. He had rightly guessed that this object was some sort of animal. Once while he was feeling for the animal his hands came in contact with some udder-like projections on its body. A thick liquid was oozing out of them. He wondered what it was. Later in a desperate state of hunger and thirst he put his mouth to one of the projections and began to suckle from it. He had never tasted anything like it in his life; it was something he could not even describe, but it was not totally unpleasant. This was the substance that was to nourish him for the rest of his days in this underground cavern. The warmth from the body of this creature comforted him for all the time he spent in darkness. In fact this was his lifeline. Without it he would have perished.

Later he began praying devotedly and fervently. He tried to concentrate and by and by he found it was easier and easier to control his mind until he was able to visualize Chenrezi. Henceforth, he spent the rest of his time chanting *Om Mani Padme Hung*, contemplating and meditating and actually beginning to experience blissful tranquillity.

One day the animal seemed to be agitated and restless. He was worried for he had now come to depend completely on this great creature for his food and warmth. He sat against it unable to meditate. A sudden thunderous noise nearly split his eardrums. It sounded like what he used to know as thunder, the roar of a dragon. What was happening? A second peal of thunder sounded even louder and the animal he was leaning on shook violently and roared forth a thundering sound so that he was thrown onto the ground. He quickly recovered himself and held onto its mane. It roared again, and on the third sound it took off with a ferocity so great that it burst through the earth and he was outside his dark prison.

Once above the surface of the earth the pilgrim jumped to the ground and landed safely on the soft snow. The brilliant light hurt his eyes and nearly blinded him. As he lifted his arms to shield his eyes, he just got a glimpse of the great greenish white serpentine creature, with its mane flying about wildly, disappearing into the clouds leaving behind a trail of flashing fire. It was truly a dragon— it looked exactly as it was depicted in the religious paintings he had gazed at in fascination in the monasteries in Ugen Choling *naktsang*!

Now it came to pass that this pilgrim finally made his way to Tibet. He sought his *tsawa lama* who was very surprised that a farmer had reached such a level of meditation on his own. On hearing of his adventure the *lama* was sure that this unusual incident was a deliberate trial, such as sometimes befalls potentially great *choepa*.

It is said that this *choepa* never returned to Bhutan but spent the rest of his life in meditation and prayer. It can be assumed that the pilgrim spent at least two to three months in the cavern, as he had started his journey in early spring and came out only with the start of the rains which is marked by thunder and lightning. This is the time when hibernating dragons emerge from their resting places and set in motion the mysterious phenomenon of fiery skies and claps of thunder that result in torrents of rain.

The elephant who had been kept starved of water for some time plunged into the river, drinking the water and spraying its parched body with its trunk.

The *Stewa Rutu* and the Elephant

A *stewa rutu* is perhaps best thought of as a water monster. It is said to be a vicious and deadly bloodthirsty creature which has the appearance of the rubbery wall of the stomach of a cow with twisting tentacles with which to grasp its victims. It is said that many many years ago there was such a deadly creature under the bridge in Wangdiphodrang. Not only was the creature vicious and bloodthirsty but it was also known to have some kind of supernatural powers. Every day some unfortunate person or cattle would fall prey to this creature which, it was said, had an insatiable appetite and would devour as many animals and humans as it could get in a day. The people in the region knew about it and they tried to keep away from the river. It was usually an unsuspecting traveler passing through Wangdiphodrang who fell prey to this monstrous creature. It was said that the prey did not have to be physically caught by the *stewa rutu*. With its supernatural powers it could actually draw the victim's blood through his or her shadow. So, every time somebody crossed the bridge and the shadow fell on the water the *stewa rutu* would hold onto it. The victim would stand on the bridge transfixed and dazed until all his strength and power was drained out. The lifeless body would then drop into the river like a block of wood. As soon as the body touched the water the *stewa rutu* would clasp its numerous tentacles around the victim and devour him. It was indeed a horrible sight and many who saw this actually happening were haunted by memories of it for many years later.

This creature was a scourge, and fear and anxiety gripped the inhabitants. One day the villagers assembled in the Wangdiphodrang *dzong* courtyard and implored the *dzongpon* to do something about the monster. "Our lives have come to a standstill ever since this creature appeared in the water. It cannot be a god; it must be a demon. We have to get rid of it," they said in unison.

Now the dzongpon was not only a very ingenious man but also one who was willing to take risks. He arranged to obtain the strongest elephant from Lhostam, the southern part of Bhutan where elephants were found in plenty at that time. As he did not tell the people his plan everyone was very curious and wondered what his next move would be. So one day when he summoned a hundred women to come forward with their frying pans, the rest of the population could not resist following the women. While the people stood at a cautious distance from the river and watched, he instructed each woman to fry a panful of sand. Then he drove the elephant into the river. The elephant who had been kept starved of water for some time plunged into the river, drinking the water and spraying its parched body with its trunk. As everyone looked on there was a sudden swift and movement in the water close to the elephant, and the next moment the *stewa rutu* had entwined its many fleshy tentacles around the hind legs of the elephant. The elephant trumpeted loudly and began to move towards the sandbank. But the *stewa rutu* seemed to possess extraordinary strength too and resisted the movement away from the depths of the water. A most grisly struggle ensued, while the silent audience watched in complete horror. The struggle went on for a long time until finally the elephant, now staggering a little, was able to walk to the sandbank with the creature still clinging to its legs. This was exactly what the *dzongpon* had hoped would happen.

The elephant stumbled and went down, first on its front legs, and then the whole body crashed under its own weight, for its body was drained of every drop of blood! The *dzongpon*, who had been watching the whole thing very attentively knew exactly what to do. As soon as the elephant's mighty body crashed to the sand, he commanded the women to pour the now red-hot sand onto the creature that still clung to the dying elephant. There were sizzling and burning noises when the brave women poured the sand onto the *stewa rutu*. It shrunk and became smaller with every panful of sand. Eventually the huge creature had shrunk to the size of a dried-up cow intestine. In fact that's just what it looked like. The only things that still appeared to be alive were its luminous saucer-like eyes that stared into space, registering nothing.

The remains of the monster were then burnt and its ashes buried under a black chorten. This scourge of Wangdiphodrang was thus removed and the people could once more travel freely to and fro and life continued as before.

Then one of its tentacles reached out and grasped Tseringmo.

The Woman who would have Eaten a *Stewa Rutu*

The Tang *Chu* which flows through the entire Tang valley is a greenish-blue river that is turbulent in most parts and calmer in others. Fish and river algae abound in the river. But fishing is frowned upon as sinful, so Tang *chu* algae have a reputation beyond the valley's boundaries. The river is a significant geographical boundary and people often refer to one another, in Tangkho, as being from the upper river, *khay totmai*, the lower river, *khay madmai*, the other side of the river, *khay tholomai*, or this side of the river, *khay stolomai*. However, all Tangpas share the folklore associated with their river.

One fairly well known story is the one about a woman who would have eaten a *stewa rutu* if it had not eaten her first. Tseringmo was collecting firewood on the banks of the Tang *chu*. As she filled her basket with the dried driftwood lying there she came across what she thought was a piece of dried meat. It looked like a dried piece of the intestine of a cow. She looked at it carefully and saw that it was a good piece. She was a poor woman and meat was a rarity in her diet so she gladly picked it up and tossed it into her basket with the firewood she had collected. "A cat must have stolen it from someone's house in Kizom," she said aloud as if to justify acquiring something that she had not worked for.

Once back home she piled up the firewood against the rickety ladder to her house and took her lucky find into the house. She filled a *chuzang*, the huge water container, and threw in the intestine to soak for a while, and then she went out to call her friend, Nadon, and ask her to come and share the night meal with her.

Tseringmo was away from home longer than she expected, for her friend was not home yet. She waited for a while and excitedly told her friend about her find and her plans. "Nadon, now I would like You to come and we can have dinner together. You can bring the rice. you must have some for didn't you just return from *tosui* in Kurtoi? We will cook it at my house. We will have rice and fried tripe."

The two women hurried back to the house very excited, like two little girls who share a secret never to be told. They hurried up the ladder and opened the door to go in. But an enormous monster that filled the room. It was a huge intestine, with numerous tentacles protruding from its body that shook and shivered as it moved about in an uncoordinated sort of way. The two women were shocked but could not move. They stood there mesmerized by the creature as it began slowly but surely to inch towards them across the kitchen floor. Then one of its tentacles reached out and grasped Tseringmo. At this moment Nadon screamed and shrieked in utter panic and dread but she could do nothing to save her friend. She ran around the village crying and shouting, "What freak is this? What monster...."

When the villagers came together and she was finally able to explain what had happened, they rushed towards the house. They did not have to go very near the house as the creature which had been fortified with fresh blood was now boldly extending its long tentacles through the windows towards the approaching people.

"Set the monster on fire," shouted a voice among the crowd and soon torches of resin wood that burns easily were being thrown at the house. A terrific blaze soon engulfed the house and the smoke rose high above the village. When the air was filled with the smell of burning and charring flesh the people knew that they had succeeded in destroying the monster.

It is believed that during heavy floods the *stewa rutu*, like other water creatures, is sometimes washed ashore. But unlike the other water creatures this monster can actually survive without water for many days by shriveling up and conserving its energy. As soon as it comes in contact with water it will grow back to its normal size again and begin its second life.

The Spirit of Necorpa

We human beings are not the sole occupiers of this world. We share this world with numerous other beings, seen and unseen. Spirits and ghosts make up a large number of the unseen beings. Some of these spirits are malicious while others are benevolent. The Bhutanese are taught to be ever mindful of the other beings so as not to bring harm to these spirits and to try and live in harmony with them. But in every Bhutanese society there are those spirits that are always resentful of human beings and readily cause havoc that disrupts the harmony of the human lives.

In the Tang valley of Bumthang there are many such spirits and even to this day not only are they acknowledged but rites and rituals appropriate to them are conducted to placate and appease them in case the people have knowingly or unknowingly incurred their wrath. One of the best known spirits of this category is Necorpa or the Pilgrim, sometimes also known as Dasho. Every known spirit has a history which explains why and how it became a malicious wandering spirit. It appears that throughout man's constant migrations the spirits moved from place to place with the human beings. Their powers rose and fell at different times in history.

Now it is said that at one time the spirit of Necorpa was rising so rapidly that the people of Tang fell into the grip of paranoia as more and more people fell ill and cattle wasted away and died. Crops failed and bridges collapsed. With every catastrophe the power and fame of Necorpa grew. Finally the people got together and after a long and somber meeting decided that something had to be done. The village elders went and beseeched the most revered lama in the region to subjugate the spirit of Necorpa.

Out came a ruffled and weak looking pigeon that was dazed and groggy.

The holy lama came and made elaborate preparations for a *gagdru*, the destructive or coercive ritual to subjugate evil or malevolent spirits. A triangular metal container or *hungkhang* was placed in front of the altar on a tripod stand. The stand was placed on a black yak-hair rug. Around the trap was placed a heap of thorny branches to prevent the spirit from escaping. The mantras of *gagdru* were chanted for days, and on the final day there came a band of men carrying torches that sparkled and flashed as they threw the *howla*, a powder made from roasted and ground decaying wood, onto the fire, and ran wildly to every room in every house. A man with a leather bag followed them, striking the bag against the ground in every nook and cranny of every house. More men carrying bags of white crystalline pebbles came following him. They threw pebbles everywhere as the man with the leather bag hit the bag on the ground. The ghost-chasing men shrieked and whistled without restraint. In the pitch darkness of the night the men, whose masked faces could only be seen in the light of the torches, looked as fearsome as the noises they made and their faces and naked upper bodies glistened with their own sweat. The lama, and his retinue followed quietly. The lama sedately ringing the bell, *dilbo*, in his left hand and waving the *dathar*, the sacred arrow, in his right hand, went around repeatedly reciting powerful and secret mantras.

When every space where any human being would ever have trod had been visited the procession made its way back to the monastery. More mantras were chanted and then the spirit of Necorpa was called by every name he was known by, and the contents of the bag, small wooden plates with inscriptions on each, were emptied out on the floor and the lama made swift and intricate hand gestures or mudras over the wooden plates and the *hungkhang*. The spirit of Necorpa was at last caught and trapped. The container was sealed both physically and spiritually.

The next day the container was taken in a solemn procession and thrown into the deepest part of the Tang *chu* which happened to be under the Kizom bridge. The villagers gathered together to thank the lama. In gratitude they offered him everything they had: a young milking cow, measures of grains and fabrics, and a small silken pouch filled to the rim with precious silver coins. Their gratitude knew no bounds.

For years and years Necorpa was spoken of as a spirit that was powerless and harmless. Then one fatal day a young cow boy was herding his cows on the banks of the river. There had been heavy rains for several days and the river was swollen. Branches and logs floated on the water and occasionally a dead fish was washed along. Chola the cowherd wanted to collect the fish to roast and pound with his chili. His lunch of *kaptang*, a flat circular bread, certainly would taste better with fish in his chili paste!

He stood on the banks of the river with a stick trying to catch a fish when he noticed a piece of metal sticking out from the sand on the bank. He promptly dropped the stick and ran towards the metal object thinking that he had found a knife or a sword. He tried to pull it out but it was stuck, so he dug furiously around the object until he was able to pull it out. It was a triangular container that was sealed on every side. He studied it for a while, rather disappointed that it was not a knife or a sword, a boy's most prized possessions. He put it to his ear and shook it, but there was no indication of anything being in it. "Perhaps I should throw it back into the river," he thought, and in fact he raised it over his shoulder in an attempt to throw it and then abruptly he changed his mind. He placed the object on a rock and pulled out his own knife and broke the *lac* seals. There was a feeble push against the lid before he could open it. A sudden excitement surged in his heart and he swiftly opened the lid. Out came a ruffled and weak looking pigeon that was dazed and groggy. It shook itself lethargically, waited a while and then fluttered into the air clumsily. As it flew away it said, "Kizom Chola, I shall never harm you and your kin." And so the spirit of Necorpa was released and was on the loose once again to wreck havoc among the people!

To this day the spirit of Necorpa holds a formidable place among the known spirits of Tang. Every body in Tang at some time or another has had to conduct placatory rites for Necorpa. True to his word the spirit of Necorpa has never harmed the people of Kizom.

Epilogue

Dingbo must never Catch up with *Dangbo* ...

We are told that *Dingbo* must never catch up with *Dangbo* for if he did then there would not be any more stories. As long as *Dangbo* is ahead of *Dingbo* there will continue to be stories. There was, however, a time in history, a long long time ago when the stories nearly ended for *Dangbo* was incapacitated and just narrowly escaped being caught by *Dingbo*.

Dangbo was running away from *Dingbo* as he had been running from time immemorial, or from the time that people began to tell stories. Suddenly he stepped on a thorn and could not run any further. He sat down and put his right foot on his left knee and inspected the sole of his foot. He right away saw the thorn that was lodged deep inside his heavily calloused sole. He could not pull it with his bare fingers. He had to have a needle. He realized to his dismay that the needle he always stuck in the collar of his *gho* for times like this was no longer there. It must have fallen out somewhere as he ran. But he would have to hurry because he knew that *Dingbo* was close behind him.

He was sitting there quite helpless when a **brokpa** passed him. Full of hope he eagerly asked, "**Ashang** Brokpa, please lend me a needle."

The *Brokpa* turned to him: "No! I won't lend you my needle," he said quite indifferently, probably unaware of the danger he was causing to the world of stories.

"Mouse, Mouse, please gnaw at the bag of the *brokpa*," requested *Dangbo* of a mouse that came and crouched near them.

"No, no, I won't gnaw at his bag," squeaked the mouse.

"Cat, Cat, catch this mouse," *Dangbo* asked a cat that had just stopped by. By now *Dangbo* was getting nervous for he knew that *Dingbo* would soon be catching up with him.

"No, no, I don't want to catch the mouse," meowed the cat.

"Dog, Dog, chase the cat," said *Dangbo* as a dog turned up, having heard the meowing cat.

"No, no, I won't chase the cat," barked the dog as he lay down to watch the growing crowd of strangers.

" Stick, Stick, beat this dog," shouted *Dangbo* loudly to a stick lying on the side of the road.

"No, no, I won't beat the dog," replied the stick lazily as he stretched out and lay deeper in the grass.

Dangbo turned desperately to the flickering fire which had been lit by some travelers who had passed this way and begged, "Fire, Fire, burn the stick."

"No, no, I won't burn the stick." replied the fire, defiantly flaming up and crackling.

Now *Dingbo* could be seen in the distance coming closer and closer. *Dangbo* had to do something before he was caught. He saw a stream and shouted, "Water, Water, put out the fire."

"No, no, I won't put out the fire," sang the water as it flowed down the stream.

Dangbo had to go on but he could not walk. He got up and took a few faltering steps and then fell back. He looked around miserably as a ram happened to come by. "Ram, Ram, drink up the water," he pleaded.

It is not quite clear whether the ram actually heard this plea or whether he was simply very thirsty but he promptly walked over to the stream and began to drink thirstily from the stream lapping up huge gulps of the water. This started up a whole chain of events and *Dangbo* escaped being caught by *Dingbo*.

As the ram began to drink the water the startled water splashed up and put out the fire. The fire flickered for a while and then rose fiercely and scorched the stick. The stick stood upright, did a quick somersault, and began to hit the dog. The dog yelped and whimpered and ran after the cat who hissed and scolded and ran after the mouse, who let out a big squeak and began to gnaw in earnest at the *brokpa's* bag. The *brokpa* seeing all this said, "Here, here, take the needle and tell the mouse to stop gnawing at my brand-new bag."

Dangbo gladly took the needle, loosened the thorn and picked it out and stood up and instantly took to his heels just as *Dingbo* reached the spot where *Dangbo* had sat. He missed *Dangbo* by a hair's breath. The great chase through time was on once again.

Thus every story must begin with *Dangbo* .... *Dingbo* or *Dangbo thik naki wenda, Dingbo thik naki wenda* ... *Dangbo* must always be ahead of *Dingbo* so that stories can follow ...

Glossary

Acchu	Unclean stream or river. Bhutanese consider a river or stream unclean if there are settlements or villages up stream.
A khai	Expression of repulsion
Acho-La-La	Acho means elder brother. The moon is often referred to as elder brother-La-La.
Ah chu chu	An expression of being cold.
Aila	Grandmother in Bumthangkha.
Ama	Mother in all dialects of Bhutan.
Aming	Maternal aunt in Bumthangkha.
Aming Niwa	Aunt mouse in Bumthangkha.
Ani/Animo	Nun.
Apa/Ap	Father.
Ara	Home-distilled liquor made from maize, wheat, barley, rice, buckwheat or millet.
Ashang	Maternal uncle.
Ashi	Title used for queens and princesses. The term is often used for ladies of the aristocracy.
Ayi wha	An expression of sadness in Bumthangkha
Ayi-di-chi	Poor thing.
Bachu	A small Tibetan cow.
Bamairuchung	Horns of mithans, often ornately decorated in gold and silver, are used as containers for oil and alcoholic drinks.
Bangchung	A small double basket made of bamboo.

192

Boden	A high mattress used as a couch or a bed, usually stuffed with dried moss, used by wealthy and high-ranking people.
Bomed	A girl or daughter but in literal translation it means "not a boy" in Bumthangkha.
Brokpa	Nomad herders.
Bumthangkha	The dialect of Bumthang in central Bhutan.
Bumthangpa khuli	A pancake from buckwheat flour. Buckwheat is the staple food of Bumthang.
Chod	A ritual during which discontented spirits are invited to feast on the practitioner's body which has been transformed into sanctified food.
Chabsang	Literally translated as "secret water," it refers to urine.
Chenrezi	The Buddha of Compassion.
Chodpa	A practitioner of a religious ritual *chod*.
Choepa	Any person who has received empowerment to perform certain religious rites and rituals.
Chu	River.
Dasho	A title usually bestowed upon a person by the king. The term is often used for men of the aristocracy.
Dermo	Demoness
Dhalham	Bhutanese knee-length boots, the upper portion being made of cloth, often elaborately embroidered, and with leather soles.
Dri	A unit of measurement (volume) used for grains and flour.
Dzong	A fortified palace usually the center for administrative as well as religious affairs
Dzongkha	Official language of Bhutan.

Dzongpon	Administrative head of a dzong.
Gho	Males dress.
Gomchen	A lay religious practitioner of the Ningmapa sect.
Jatsam	Female progeny of a mithan bull (Bos frontalis) and a Bhutanese local cow.
Kaira	A woven belt.
Kaphe	Flour made of roasted barely or wheat.
Karmatekpa	A rice variety considered to be of low quality.
Katar	White silk ceremonial scarf used on auspicious occasions.
Kira	Woman's dress
Koma	Brooches used to fasten the *kira* at the shoulders.
Kurtoip	Dialect of Kurtoi in the northeastern region of Bhutan.
Lagi	A long-sleeved white undershirt is worn under a *gho*. The sleeve ends (*lagi*) are folded back over the sleeves of the *gho*.
Lawang	An open container usually made of brass or copper which is filled with mustard oil. A wick is placed in the oil and it is used as a lamp.
Lopon	Teacher.
Lu	Subterranean beings.
Luyi gyalpo	King of the subterranean world.
Matha	Woolen fabric of red, green, and blue checks.
Melted in the sun and solidified in the shade	A typical Bhutanese expression for somebody who is extremely beautiful. Someone who is soft and fair is considered beautiful as opposed to farm women who are

generally tanned and have rough skins due to the exposure to sun and wind.

Migoi	Yeti or the abominable snowman.
Mimi	Grandfather in Bumthangkha.
Mithan	A semi-domesticated animal (Bos forntalis) similar to cattle.
Monlo Karchung	The mountain pass leading into Tibet from Bumthang.
Moringmo	Derogatory expression for woman.
Naktsang	Very large houses belonging to landed families.
Nga	A big drum used during religious ceremonies.
Nyda	Hosts. A reciprocal system of hosting between Bhutanese and Tibetans.
Om Mani Padme Hung	The mantra of Avalokiteshvara or Chenrezi.
Phob	A wooden cup. Most Bhutanese still have their individual cup and use it regularly during meals for liquids and *tsaoem.*
Phuta	A unit of measurement (approximately 350–400 ml) used for grains and flour. This measuring tool is used daily to measure the grains and flour according to the number of persons sharing a meal.
Rolong	A corpse that is revived after death and possessed by a malevolent spirit.
Singchang	Alcoholic drink made from fermented wheat, barley, buckwheat, or maize.
Sinpo	Flesh-eating spirits that roamed the earth freely until Guru Padmasambhava subdued them and exiled them to another world, *sinpoiyul.*

Sinpoiyul	Land of the *sinpos*.
Sog	The life-force.
Thro zangs	Open containers of various sizes made from an alloy. The often richly engraved utensils are considered very valuable by the Bhutanese.
Tosui	During the rice harvest people from higher elevations where no rice grows go to glean as well as to barter for rice in the lower rice-growing areas.
Tsagye	Slow and dull-witted.
Tsamkhang	Hermitage.
Tsangmo	A verse of four lines.
Tsaoem	A stew-like dish made from any vegetable, meat, or cheese.
Tsawa lama	A person's main teacher of religion, also referred to as the root teacher.
Tsen	Aboriginal deities of Tibet and Bhutan who have become the guardians of the Buddhist teachings. They are believed to live in rocky areas and the color associated with them is red. In religious art they can be recognized as red men mounted on red horses.
Tsog	A generic term used for biscuits made of wheat flour which are usually fried in oil.
Wangdi dzongpon	Administrator of Wangdiphodrang.
Whay	Hey you.
Yaah lama	An expression of surprise, *o lama*.
Yuva	Large containers woven from strips of bamboo or cane, used to store grains
Za	A group of spirits who are known as protectors of the Buddhist teachings. They are associated with the stars and influence the

human nervous system, they cause and cure paralysis, strokes and other ailments of the nervous system. They are depicted in religious art in many colors.

Zah Fungal growths or burls on trees which, when turned into cups and bowls, have intricate patterns. The Bhutanese value *zah* cups (*phobs*) and bowls very highly and they are considered to be heirlooms.

Zahphi phobs *Phobs* made of *zah*.

Zang Huge open containers made of brass or copper used for storing and cooking during special occasions for large crowds

Zi One of the most precious stones found only in Tibet and valued highly as a precious ornament in Tibet, Bhutan, Sikkim, Nepal, Ladhak, and Tawang.

Zimpon A person who is responsible for the personal welfare of the *penlop*.

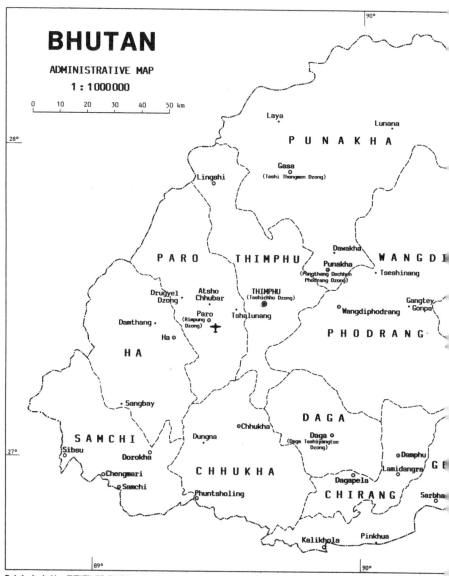

BHUTAN

ADMINISTRATIVE MAP

1 : 1000000

0   10   20   30   40   50 km

90°

28°

Laya

Lunana

P U N A K H A

Gasa
○
(Tashi Thongmen Dzong)

Lingshi
○

P A R O

T H I M P H U

Dawakha

Punakha
○
(Pungthang Dechhen
Phodrang Dzong)

W A N G D I

· Tseshinang

Drugyel
Dzong ·

Atsho
Chhubar
·

THIMPHU
(Tashichho Dzong)
◉

Gangtey
· Gonpa

Damthang ·

Paro
(Rimpung ○
Dzong)

Tshalunang

Wangdiphodrang
○

Ha ○

P H O D R A N G ·

H A

Sangbay

D A G A

S A M C H I

Dungna

○Chhukha

Daga ○
(Daga Tashiyangtse
Dzong)

○Damphu

27°

Sibsu
○

Dorokha
○

Lamidangra ·

G

○Chengmari

C H H U K H A

Dagapela
·

○ Samchi

Phuntsholing

C H I R A N G

Sarbha
○

Kalikhola

Pinkhua

89°

90°

Printed at the SURVEY OF BHUTAN, First Edition, 1988

91°

LEGEND

—·—·—	International Boundary
— — —	Dzongkhag (District) Boundary
	Paved Road
	Unpaved Road/ under Construction
◉	Capital
⊙	Dzongkhag (District) Headquarter
○	Dungkhag (Sub- district) Headquarter
·	Town, Village
✈	Airport

28°

Singye Dzong

hedang ·

Khenpa Dzong

L H U N T S H I

⊙ Lhuntshi

B U M T H A N G

Kurjey · Nangnang ·

Jakar ⊙

Ura

S A

Tashi Yangtse ⊙

Sakteng ○

Radi ·

Dametsi · Tashigang ⊙

Mongar ⊙

Gyepozhing ·

T A S H I G A N G

· Shemgang

M O N G A R

Wamrong ○ Thrimshing ○

Pemagatsel ·

P E M A- GATSEL

S A M D R U P

G

S H E M G A N G

J O N G K H A R

27°

Daifam ○

Panbang ○

·hug

lai

○ Nganglam

Samdrup Jongkbar ⊙ Bhangtar ○

91° 92°